*The Blue Mist* is a guidebook on human factors told in a personnel way. Tony Laws takes you on a journey through human factors training which is based on his own experiences and research, that has come from a career in military and civilian aviation industries that spans over thirty years and in many parts of the world.

He has unique aviation experience from a human factor's perspective, having qualified as an aircraft engineer, a pilot, and a technical crew member. A licensed Crew Resource Management Instructor (CRMI), he is also passionate about training, he has developed the *Blue Mist* concept for human factors training in all industries and continues to actively teach human factors.

The author lives on a small rural property in Southwest Victoria and enjoys fishing, walking his dogs and photography. He is currently working on his first set of novels, a trilogy based around characters during the Second World War.

To Kaylene and Yarraman, my sanctuary in a crazy world and to all those people who put their lives at risk in the pursuit of saving others.

Tony Laws

# THE BLUE MIST

## A New Insight into Human Factors

AUSTIN MACAULEY PUBLISHERS™

LONDON • CAMBRIDGE • NEW YORK • SHARJAH

A CIP catalogue record for this title is available from the British Library.

ISBN 9781398465947 (Paperback)
ISBN 9781398465954 (ePub e-book)

www.austinmacauley.com

First Published 2023
Austin Macauley Publishers Ltd®
1 Canada Square
Canary Wharf
London
E14 5AA

I would like to thank and acknowledge the many people I have had the great privilege to have worked with over the years. In the navy and the various companies I have been associated with since leaving the service.

My family and friends have greatly supported me and put up with my being away from home on long occasions. My father has been a substantial influence in my life, and my mother was always there to listen. I miss them terribly, and they were taken from us too soon. My twin brother Steve has always been a great source of inspiration to me, and I am still amazed as he always has, wherever I am in the world, visited me, often on his own. Even more impressive is that he is a wheelchair user; it never seems to bother him, and he has stoically embraced life since being paralysed in a motorbike accident at the age of 20.

I could not have written this without the help and encouragement from the following people. My partner Kaylene, Hannah and Freya, my wonderful daughters, Alan Rose and Paul Rowland, my original business partners in Blue Mist HFC. All the people who have proofread my dyslexic writing over the years, far too many to acknowledge personally! Especially Mairead Rodgers, who patiently and diligently assisted me in producing the original manuscript.

Chris Bond, who was my mentor during my initial years in Australia, patiently listening to my frustrations and difficulties when I needed to get things off my chest (I think everyone needs a Chris Bond in their lives). His patience and calm, steady advice when things were getting tough are so very much appreciated.

Mr John Harvey, my technical and applied mathematics teacher at Arbroath High School. Who taught me the fundamentals of digital technology when the first calculators appeared? My parents gave me a Casio Ti SR10 for Christmas in 1975; he allowed me to use it during class and came out with the best phrase ever on digital technology use. "Mr Laws put garbage in, get garbage out".

I have had the absolute privilege to work with all the aviators, aircraft engineers, and support staff over the years. I have always said a company's best assets are their people, and we achieve our goals as a team, not individuals. I have been lucky to have been recognised for my work in Search and Rescue. I could not have achieved this without the teamwork of so many others. Everybody counts, not just the so-called heroes that operate the helicopter.

# Chapter 1
# An Introduction

I wanted to write this book for some time now, yet I can't explain why. Like most people, I lead a busy life, kids, work, socialising and somehow a reason not to do it always seems better than a reason to do it. I feel the necessity has now been thrust upon me. It has happened because of events surrounding my working life as an aviator. I have been flying for most of my working life; my occupation as aircrew has been rewarding and enjoyable. However, it has been, at times, both heart-breaking and tragic. I have lost over 40 friends in aviation accidents throughout the past 35 years, mainly in the military. What is strange is that only one has been from direct military action; the rest has been from aircraft accidents.

Since leaving the navy in 2001, I have been heavily involved in the Search and Rescue (SAR), in active flying roles, training and management. SAR has been a passion; you can't help being passionate about it. To save a human life is the most rewarding job satisfaction a person can achieve in their working life.

Traditionally, the SAR community has been very fortunate with accidents compared to other areas of emergency services, such as emergency medical service (EMS) or helicopter emergency medical service (HEMS).

When I teach crew resource management (CRM) to SAR people, I often hear, 'Why do we need to do this? We are a clear example of great CRM and teams working well together.'

In some matters, yes, they are correct as they often display excellent examples of teamwork, leadership, decision making and many other aspects of CRM. However, they still have accidents and incidents.

The year 2013 was for the SAR helicopter community, an *annus horribilis*. At least five fatal-winching accidents occurred during the year. They were ranging from the very public death of a winchman during a demonstration in Saudi Arabia to a casualty falling to his death after slipping out of the rescue strop in a remote area of Victoria, Australia. In 2017 an Irish Coast Guard Sikorsky S92 Search and Rescue helicopter, one of the most sophisticated rescue helicopters globally, was lost with its crew on a night mission off the Irish West Coast. The task was to provide mutual support to another S92 which was on the primary mission to recover an injured fisherman. We will look at this accident a little later in the book; the tragedy, however, is a common one; the rescuer or rescuers die trying to save the victims.

I have often been in awe of people who dedicate their lives to rescuing others in distress as well as the broader community of the emergency services. One thing I have learned, every rescue involves many organisations and is quite complicated. It is very much a team effort and without this synergy, a casualty recovery can become very difficult and prone to more complications when trying to achieve a successful outcome.

Since I have been looking at the wider community and other industries, I've noticed a theme of human factors in all accidents and incidents. To put it bluntly: People cause accidents; very rarely do the machines they operate cause them. People create culture and organisations that often influence those within these organisations to cause said accidents. The system effectively sets up the catalyst, which then puts the consequences and components together to start a chain of events that result in an accident.

Human factors are the key, I believe, to proper health and safety. We tend to concentrate on checking things and setting systems up to stop accidents. However, we forget that the thing fundamentally causing accidents is the human element—the people. See, the thing is, people don't get up in the morning and say to themselves, 'Today I am going to cause an accident.'

We need to concentrate on the people themselves and show them how and why they make mistakes. Teach them how to behave and identify error-producing conditions. Teach them how to communicate effectively so once they see a situation that could lead to an accident, they can be assertive and express their concerns.

Aviation has been the lead industry in human factors for some time now and recently the commercial helicopter industry has also embraced CRM. Crew resource management was introduced into the commercial fixed-wing world in the 1970s when the civil aviation industry badly needed a safety system that looked at the human element in accidents. This safety model has become the adopted practice by many countries.

In the 1970s, they had captains who predominantly trained in the military, producing highly skilled pilots or, as aviators often describe it, 'great stick and rudder' pilots. Meaning they had excellent skills as a pilot; however, their skills with people were often dreadful. One CRM program I participated in showed a video called "The Right Stuff". This was a slightly sarcastic parody on the movie of the same name about the space program in America. The CRM program was hinting that old military single pilots who flew fighters were the right stuff for the space program but not the right stuff for the airline industry. They wanted their captains to manage their crew, be a team player when needed and be more team focused when times were not so critical; for example, sorting out where the crew could eat during a stopover.

I can say that in my 33 years as an aviator, I have seen some atrocious examples of CRM. Captains who have been nothing better than obnoxious bullies unable to handle being questioned about their decisions. Thankfully, these dinosaurs are slowly leaving aviation through retirement or finally embracing CRM training.

Over time, some of my fellow CRM organisers and I have facilitated courses with this breed of aviator and met with stony silence. The new generation also throws up the odd pilot with this quality in their personality, often described as the alpha male or type A Personality. In my own experience, I have only endured this once or twice in the modern aviation industry.

Aviation's first high-profile accident in the 1970s prompted action as it listed human factors as the root cause. Originally CRM stood for cockpit resource management and changing to crew resource management after identifying that several accidents having significant influences from beyond the cockpit. For example, an air stewardess spotted an engine on fire and was ignored by the pilots.

Political correctness has forced change; it is no longer the pilots; it is the "flight crew". Likewise, we don't have airline stewardesses and stewards; we have the "cabin crew". It's no longer air crewmen on search and rescue missions; instead, we have the "technical crew".

CRM has been an evolving process as we discover new human factors influencing our safety. Automation in the cockpit systems has been a significant change in the way we train. Built to improve safety, however, we have discovered that the mismanagement of automation can lead to accidents and in severe cases actually be a root cause of accidents.

Regulatory bodies led by the Federal Aviation Administration (FAA) in the United States of America and international bodies, such as the International Civil Aviation Organisation have created new CRM programs. These all revolve around core subjects (see them in Table 1).

I have added a new organisation to the human factors arena, the World Health Organisation as the medical industry has apparent similarities with aviation. A 24-hour operation, complex tasks that are life-threatening and a diverse number of skilled people working together to achieve a difficult task.

I believe it is a matter of time before new industries like the energy and resource industries see that human factors training is critical in their safety programs. Any industry can benefit from this training—no matter what you provide, you need a human element to facilitate it. When there is a human element, you always have the potential for an accident. Each industry and organisation is unique and may have slightly different priorities in their core elements. There are two other training systems within the safety aviation system: the aircrew have (CRM), and the engineers have (MRM—maintenance resource management). For clarification, engineers have slightly different areas where mistakes occur, although the main principles are the same.

| | Federal Aviation Administration (USA) | Civil Aviation Authority (UK) | International Civil Aviation Organisation (International) | World Health Organisation (International) |
|---|---|---|---|---|
| 1 | Company safety culture | Information processing | Sensory—perceptual factures | Organisational culture |
| 2 | Information processing | Perception | Medical and physical factors | Managerial leadership |
| 3 | Threat and error management | Vigilance and monitoring | Knowledge and skill factors | Communication |
| 4 | Human error | Attention | Personality and safety attitude factors | Teamwork |
| 5 | Communication | Human error, skill, reliability, and error management | Judgement—risk decision factors | Team leadership |
| 6 | Leadership/teamwork | Workload | Communication/ crew co-ordination factors | Situational awareness |
| 7 | Decision making | Surprise and startle | Design/system factors | Decision making |
| 8 | Stress, stress management, fatigue and vigilance | Situational awareness | Supervisory factors | Stress |
| 9 | Cultural factors | Decision making | | Fatigue |
| 10 | Automation | Stress in aviation | | Work environment |
| 11 | Specific type-related differences | Sleep and fatigue | | |
| 12 | Case-based studies | Personality and cultural differences | | |
| 13 | | Teamwork | | |
| 14 | | Leadership | | |
| 15 | | Communication | | |

**Table 1**

From Table 1, you can see that each organisation has many common elements such as teamwork. If we break the

14

table down and join together the common threads, what remains are the proficiencies that a person needs to be competent at human factors (see Figure 1). You will note that "communication" is in the centre and the other skills branch out around it. Because you cannot achieve any of the other tasks without good communication, that is the key to competency.

**Figure 1**

These competencies are the building blocks to achieving a safe and happy working environment. If we have high morale, a safety-conscious workforce, a workforce aware of human factors and positive safety culture, the workplace can become more efficient and safer. Human-factors training is a catalyst to decrease accidents and incidents and create a safer environment for everyone.

The core elements are now more generalised and not so aviation centric. Not so much crew resource management but it becomes team resource management (TRM). TRM covers the broader working community, who can hopefully adapt and embrace human factors training.

The search and rescue aviation community has adopted this training and I have personally developed a CRM program explicitly looking at the SAR helicopter crews. The knowledgeable SAR crew is the classic teamwork model: communication, decision making, situational awareness and problem-solving; all the traditional CRM topic headings.

Despite this, in 2013, the SAR community had five deaths during winching operations and according to the Aviation Safety Network database on aircraft incidents, 44 deaths in SAR/EMS/HEMS related accidents.

During my research in investigating these accidents, the causation of the accident is the rescue people themselves, who only went to work on any day with the sole intention of helping their fellow human beings. Did they think that whilst they conducted each operation that caused their demise that they were doing anything wrong? Probably not. The fundamental aspect that I believe occurred in all the accidents, which I will explore in this book, is not one person went out to hurt themselves or anyone else. They all did what they thought was their best; I salute all of them because they made no mistakes. They simply fell prey to that instinct, which is part of our core DNA as humans: to save another human being. That, in itself, is the ultimate reward.

Involved in helicopter SAR over the many years, I admit to having made mistakes, wrong decisions and have taken risks, which thankfully have turned out okay. Experience over the years has made me wiser; however, you never stop learning in this world of aviation. Take this journey together through this book; I hope that you, the reader, can benefit from the life lessons that appear through the stories of those who have gone before us.

It is not my intention by any means to pick fault with the actions of others during a highly stressful and possibly dangerous event. Simply because those individuals did not know they had done anything wrong at the time, they were just a victim of circumstance. In most cases, people just fall into that string of events, the error chain that results in undesirable consequences. Thankfully, in the modern age of health and safety, we have many control measures in each office or workspace to prevent the average human from making such mistakes.

I have been truly blessed in that I have been very privileged to work around the world in various countries. I have worked as an aviator with military and civilian occupations, assisting the emergency services of those countries. I have worked with very experienced and inexperienced people in different professions. It is giving me a privileged position and a perspective that I could not have seen otherwise. I am not brash or wish to be sanctimonious; I only hope that my colleagues, friends, fellow emergency service brethren and the broader global industry can benefit from its message by reading this book.

# Chapter 2
# What is Blue Mist?

Blue Mist: what is it and where did it originate? As I have got older and wiser, I have tried to define what it is that seems, for want of a better word, to make everyone "silly" during rescues or emergencies.

I discovered this phrase by talking to a friend who was a policeman. Somehow, we began discussing what I was working on at the time. I described my loss for a word to summarise how people become worked up and emotional, resulting in mistakes during rescue situations. He said he knew exactly what I meant and described the emotion the police come across when people commit violent crimes, known as "red mist".

The Oxford English Dictionary describes this phenomenon as red mist. Its origin from the supposed physiological effect of blood rushing to the head in a moment of anger or excitement, 'A fit of extreme anger that temporarily clouds a person's judgement.'

From understanding this, I found the perfect phrase to describe the phenomenon I witnessed—blue mist. The emotion we have taken away the logical risk assessment thought process when a human or in some cases an animal life is threatened.

A typical example of blue mist can be found in military gallantry award citations, i.e. 'Corporal Smith with complete disregard for his own safety ran across the exposed ground under fire to rescue his comrade.' I have read it enough in my own colleagues' gallantry citations to see the emergency service equivalent.

As humans, we risk assess everything in daily life. The Darwinian Theory says we have evolved from early ape-like creatures and modern psychiatry suggests that we still have the primal instinct of "fight or flight". However, a split-second decision will prepare our bodies to execute either option as adrenalin surges through our veins.

A typical example is our approach to the amber traffic light; do we speed up and run through before it turns red or goes with the safer option and slow and come to a stop? We go through a mental thought process and sum up the options between risk and reward. The greater the reward, the more likely we will take the risk necessary to achieve it. If you add competition to the equation, you will be more likely to run the risk and speed through the hypothetical traffic lights.

If you measure risk over reward, what greater reward is there than saving a life? I still find it incredibly sad when emergency service personnel, who dedicate their lives to aiding human beings in distress, are killed in the process.

In 2006 the National Transport Safety Board (NTSB) of the USA published a special report due to its concern over the high fatality rate amongst helicopter emergency medical service (HEMS) and emergency medical service (EMS) crews. A shocking fact was the very next year in 2007, these HEMS operations became the most dangerous profession in

North America, overtaking deep-sea fishing in deaths per 100,000.

In 2007 there was a total of 113 deaths in HEMS aircraft accidents. We improved in 2013, reducing to 18 deaths in HEMS related accidents. However, the five deaths in winch-related incidents are unprecedented as winching-related fatal accidents had been infrequent up until now.

In the UK, the last death during a SAR mission was Billy Deacon, a Bristow winchman based in Sumburgh, Shetland Islands. He died during the rescue operation of the MV Green Lily crew on 19 November 1997. I met Billy at an air crewman association weekend just before he died, a truly genuine guy. Billy's death was the first since RAF winchman Dave Bullock and pilot William Olson, who both lost their lives during the rescue of an A10 Thunderbolt jet survivor on 18 November 1980. Although incredibly tragic, both accidents resulted in improvements in rescue equipment and procedures. Such as the J-knife, twin hoist systems and winchman communications.

One apparent factor in HEMS and EMS is the sheer volume of operations. In North America, a HEMS/EMS helicopter takes off on a mission every 30 seconds. If you look at the statistics, the accident rate is declining compared with the rate per every 100,000 flying hours. Could it be that, concerning winch accidents, there is an increase in the volume of winch-related rescues?

The president of the Helicopter Association International at the time, Matt Zuccarro, stated, 'Despite what we might see on the news, the truth is that the helicopter EMS sector of the industry is not experiencing a disproportionate number of accidents…it's just that these accidents are such a high profile that people assume EMS operations have a poor accident history.'

The NTSB, the UK's Civil Aviation Authority (CAA) and New Zealand's CAA have brought legislation and recommendations into effect to improve the section of aviation's safety record. The UK's CAA CAP 999 is a document that addresses explicitly emergency service aviation governance. The impact this legislation is having on emergency service helicopter operations is probably too early to be recognised. However, in some countries, there is always a "get out of jail free card".

In Australia, this comes in the form of a rule called "mercy flight". Meaning the captain of an aircraft can fly what has deemed an irregular flight to save a life. There are some prerequisites; for instance, there must be no other way of conducting the flight, which complies with standard aviation regulations. E.g. a mercy flight can be called to save a gravely ill person and may die in the next few hours, located in a remote area when the weather is below minima. These rules put enormous pressure on the crew, especially the captain of the aircraft.

I have read many accident reports over the year's pilots and crews saying they let the patient's condition affect their judgement. Quite often, pressure on the rescue crew or emergency services is self-induced, perceived pressure brought about by the casualties' precarious position, severe pressure to counter and will be discussed later in the book.

Blue mist can be seen in many accidents in the emergency services from high-speed car chases to helicopter crashes while transferring patients. The wider industry and other occupations have their accidents, such as the train crash because the driver was speeding, the scissors left in a patient during surgery or the roof tiller who falls off the roof. The fundamental link to all these incidents is a sequence of events or error chains that lead to the fateful event.

The answer may seem very simple—break the chain. I do wish it were that easy; however, the very nature of the blue mist makes it difficult to see these errors unfolding. Unfortunately, if there were just one interruption to any chain, then the accident would never occur in the first place.

In most cases, the emergency service personnel do not think they are doing anything wrong; in fact, they believe what they are doing is completely normal. A phrase I have often heard is, *We are on a SAR mission; we can do what we want, we don't have to follow the rules.* In some countries, this may be true but the critical mistake may be as simple as feeling invincible or an "it won't happen to me" mentality.

The average emergency service personnel is highly professional, highly motivated and possesses a strong sense of duty and a desire to be needed, alongside a solid need to be stimulated. These combinations can often lead to the tendency to say yes rather than no. These are also the perfect conditions for the blue mist to form and cloud better judgement in answering yes rather than the logical and safe answer of no.

The SAR team, as I have mentioned, is relatively large. It is not simply the flight crew and medics or winch crew. The medical dispatcher, the chief pilot, the doctor requesting the transfer, the oil company rig manager, the hospital administrator, it goes on and on. All are subject to blue mist and for that very reason, they can see blue mist forming and stop that error chain. For example, is the patient stable enough to wait until the morning when the weather has improved?

In really tragic cases, the emergency personnel die and the patient lives because their condition was not as life-threatening as first perceived or transmitted to the rescue personnel. Therefore, it is vital that all emergency service staff learn the signs of blue mist and become self-aware to prevent these error chains from ever unfolding.

# Chapter 3
# Cognitive Failure

Often in life we make what can only be described in layman's terms as a silly mistake. Scientists call this cognitive failure. I have been guilty of this myself and I have witnessed others commit this elementary human behaviour.

What is cognitive failure? To describe it simplistically, I will recall a personal anecdote. I held the inaugural meeting of my new company a few years ago with the co-founders. We decided to have a coffee and some lunch in a small bar in Subiaco, Western Australia. When one of my co-founders talked, he asked me to pass the milk jug during the meeting. However, instead of pouring the milk into his coffee, he poured it onto his fries. We all found it very amusing, albeit very embarrassing for him and a perfect example of cognitive failure.

If we dissect this event, there are many theories as to how this could have happened. They range from very complex neuropsychological analysis to simply explaining it as a silly lapse of judgement. What occurred was a concentration lapse during a learned motor response, having poured milk into his coffee a thousand times over and developed the appropriate "muscle music" to achieve this task. However, some factors at that time distracted him, interfering with his concentration.

A common element in cognitive failure is a tendency called cognitive bias. Our brain starts to think in a certain way and rely on previous memories, leading it to believe it sees what it expects. Scientific papers and books describe several biases, such as confirmation bias. Your brain starts to search for previous information stored in its memory centres to confirm what you are seeing. By definition, 'The tendency to interpret new evidence as confirmation of one's existing beliefs or theories.'

Research on this bias has focused on people's opinions rather than the physical world. One research team used a political campaign to study this bias. When given false information about the candidate they least liked, they tended to ignore the positive input and even searched for information to discredit them.

In everyday life, some days we are deep in thought and some we are not. Say you walk down the same street every morning and pass a familiar object like a lamppost. On the days we are aware, we take in more of the environment we pass by. We may notice the lamppost on these less thought-concentrated days. Now, if you increase concentration on issues at work or home, your brain becomes lazy and assumes the picture of the environment is the same as always, and you may not notice the lamppost.

A similar experience occurred during a helicopter ditching in the North Sea. The search and rescue helicopter in Den Helder ditched, returning to its base. In the rear of the cabin, the technical crew carried out their emergency drills, jettisoned the doors and attempted to get the life rafts to work. Due to a mechanical failure, the life rafts did not deploy.

Obviously an extremely stressful time for them, coupled with the frustration of the mechanical failure. When asked in the debrief, 'How would you deploy the life rafts?' They became convinced that you could deploy them from inside the cabin. In this particular make of helicopter, the only internal operating method was in the cockpit. Interestingly, other team members, including myself, were also asked the same question and some answered that yes, the handle was on the inside. One explanation for their actions was the type of helicopter and how it differed from the aircraft in their initial training that they had experience operating.

In this particular aircraft, you could operate the rafts from inside the cabin using a handle that was similar in shape to the door jettison handle on the ditched aircraft located inside the cabin. Had the crewmen simply reverted to previous memory in their highly stressful time?

The outcome of this accident was a new drill that helps to develop "muscle music" and reflexes in emergencies through identifying particular emergency handles and equipment regularly.

At the start of my flying career, we held pool drills every three months and this was relaxed to every six months a few years later. I must admit that my natural reflexes over time when I conducted these drills became more and more instinctive. In the civilian world, emergency procedures practised on an annual basis. Now I can't say for sure but I suspect this is due to finances. In my opinion—solely a personal viewpoint—this does not seem adequate. I have now been held responsible for conducting these drills as a civilian trainer and I am pretty shocked that some aircrew lacks the intuitive knowledge and need to be walked through these drills and tests. Further to this, in the civilian world, we don't go too deep into the survival aspects of emergencies instead of the military, emphasising this and practising it regularly.

I was going to call this chapter "The missing SAR bag affair". I was referring to a personal event that still today brings back emotive memories. As an overall event, there were many human-factor traits and like most significant incidents, many minor events that led up to it. This experience was my first personal exposure to cognitive failure. My brain is tricking me and allowing me to see what I wanted to see. It covered a lot of human-factor elements as well, such as task focusing.

I was the on-duty aircrew officer (the modern term for this role) and my role was to assist the aircraft commander with co-pilot duties, such as checklists and navigation, the other member of the crew was the search and rescue diver. This diver was the pointy end of the operation and was responsible for the physical rescue of survivors while we shared joint responsibility for the equipment.

Our work schedule was a 24-hour shift, which commenced at 1.00 in the afternoon and ended at 1.00 pm the following day. At 9.00 pm, we would go home and return to work at 7.30 am the next day to complete our shift. On this particular day, the incident happened during the morning part of our shift; although the previous day's shift had a significant influence on the events of that morning.

The previous day we had an experienced SAR pilot on shift with us and had a trainee pilot flying—new to SAR but very experienced. The new pilot had to complete a successful final check flight, allowing him to conduct missions as a qualified SAR commander. We had an operational SAR task that afternoon to pick up an injured sailor and the flight went according to plan with two pilots, a trainer and the new pilot. Due to the sailor's injuries, we had to clean and disinfect the stretcher covered in blood. The diver and I washed it thoroughly and then wiped all the parts with disinfectant and left it to dry in the drying room. The rest of the afternoon shift went without incident and the trainee pilot was signed off to fly on his own as a qualified SAR pilot.

I had noticed over the period that the diver had not been his usual self and knew he was experiencing some marital issues. We laughed this off as he was a bit of a colourful character and put it down to normal behaviour.

The following morning, we all arrived to work and set about our duties. One of the first things that happen is the aircraft is started up and checked by the pilot and the winch operator. We did this and found the helicopter was unserviceable and required a change of aircraft, which means swopping all the search and rescue equipment from the broken plane to a serviceable one.

After the diver and I began to swap the kit over, the pilot asked if I could go over the operations room control console with all the operation phones and planning data. We had one last bit of kit to transfer, so I asked the diver to finish off the swap for me.

I explained the operations phone console and the direct lines to the emergency service operations rooms as if by magic, the direct line from the coastguard rang and I answered it. We had a job; a diver located some forty miles away with a suspected heart problem and possible bend during his rushed ascent to the surface.

We took the position details and the coast guard asked us to wait for a doctor to arrive from the air station sickbay. After we confirm a call, the first thing we do is press an alarm bell that alerts the base that we have a job. The weather was not good and my role was to navigate the aircraft to the vessel's position with the ill diver.

The doctor turned up and off we went, flying below the cloud level, around 500ft. The forward visibility was about 800m. However, we were in open water and had sufficient visibility at the speed we were flying to give us ample time to avoid obstructions, such as large ships. I was soon in contact by radio with the vessel and used the homer to get an accurate bearing on his radio transmissions. By calling the ship to do a slow count to ten and back, we can obtain a precise direction and displays on the homing instrument as a vertical bar. When the bar is steady and in the middle of the display, you are flying directly at the object that is transmitting. Everything was going according to plan at this stage and I was feeling pretty good with myself.

Soon enough, starting to appear out of the mist in the distance, I could see the vessel. At that point, my whole world collapsed. I felt a tap on my shoulder; it was the SAR diver; he mouthed something at me that I couldn't understand. I asked him to say again, 'No SAR bag,' the final item of kit we had needed to transfer.

The bag contained some vital pieces of kit, such as harnesses and strops used in the rescue. Fortunately, we had some spare in a bag attached to the cabin wall. I could conduct the recovery but there would be some risk. As it was calm and the vessel was not moving much, I elected to continue.

We informed the doctor of our intentions and we decided to recover the ill diver by utilising the stretcher. I lowered a hi-line—a rope with a weighted bag attached to the winch hook—this allows better references for the pilots as they can be further away from the vessel and the vessel's crew can haul on the line and pull the hook, or person on the winch hook, towards them.

The SAR diver made it safely on board the vessel and I went to prepare the stretcher. Another shiver went down my spine, no strops on the stretcher. A discussion with the doctor and the SAR diver led us to recover the ill diver using two rescue strops in the hypothermic recovery method, one strop under the armpits and one under the knees so the survivor is retrieved in a more horizontal position.

He was soon safely on board and once we were in a safe normal flight condition, the doctor examined the patient. He was a young male and was assessed as not being critical but would require a period of time in the decompression chamber back in Portsmouth.

The doctor we had on board was a surgeon captain and the head of the medical department. To say our efforts did not amuse him was an understatement. As soon as we returned to base, he was out of the aircraft and straight up to the squadron commanding officer's office to criticise our unprofessionalism.

I completed the post-task paperwork and then stood by for the inevitable consequences. The squadron public address system sounded a series of messages. First to be summoned to the boss's office, the chief crewman, then the pilot, then the SAR diver and finally, me. The boss was stern and not impressed with our conduct. He then surprised me by saying that the SAR diver had taken full responsibility and had explained that the pilot and I were busy when I had asked him to complete the duty change.

I was asked to leave and returned to the crew room. Truthfully, I was mortified and felt incredibly guilty about the diver assuming all the blame and taking it all on the chin. I can't recall what happened then, only that the diver had been sent home.

I found out later that the night before the job, the diver had left his wife. He confessed to me that he had no significant sleep that night. My immediate response was, 'Why didn't you tell me?'

Looking back, I have dissected that job time and time again and while there are obvious mistakes, like all mishaps, incidents or accidents, many small events seemed to conspire against us. Despite this, I still feel the pilot and I could have prevented this from happening. So why didn't we? Cognitive failure, mental bias and loss of task focus, to name but a few. The SAR diver was the weak link in the error chain due to stress and fatigue from his marriage break-up.

What I have done is identify the links in the error chain and listed them below.

1. The messy rescue the previous afternoon, which necessitated the washing of the kit.
2. The lack of spare kit on-base constituted having to wash dirty gear.
3. The pilot was brand new to search and rescue operations and still a little unfamiliar with the operations room.
4. The marginal weather, which forced me to concentrate on my navigation tasks.

5. The bad timing of the job, first thing in the morning—any other time, I would have gone back and helped the diver.

6. Why did the pilot and I not notice the dispatcher harnesses were not hanging up? We were too tasked focused.

7. Fatigue played a significant part in the diver's concentration.

8. The stress from his marriage break-up was distracting the diver's attention.

9. A change in the usual procedure for a duty aircraft change as I left before the end of it to take the pilot through the operations room equipment.

10. The rest of the crew and his fellow squadron workers being unaware of the diver's wellbeing and personal issues.

I could probably have found many more if we sat down together and micro-analysed that day. However, if you look at it as a whole and then instigate a change to any of those events, it could have changed the outcome significantly and possibly prevented the event in the first place.

The SAR mission was a success; the young diver did not have a heart condition and released without any further treatment after his spell in the decompression chamber. His condition was more to do with the copious pints of lager and a curry he had consumed the night before.

Although no one was significantly injured or died and there was no damage to the aircraft or property, there was significant damage done to the reputation of the SAR unit.

This a natural consequence and one that can lead to perceived pressure on all personnel involved.

There were several examples of cognitive failure in the missing SAR bag affair. To name two, mental bias and simple task focusing are fundamental to what blue mist is all about. They cloud one's usual cognitive processes when faced with a medical emergency unusual situation; we can't see for the blue mist.

I hope by looking at this case study one can see that we do not go out with the intent to get ourselves in these situations. Almost 100% of the time it's small events that contribute to a significant and sometimes catastrophic, life-changing event. Sometimes, life indeed does conspire to make you fail.

# Chapter 4
# Situational Awareness

A common cause of aviation accidents is the phenomenon known as a breakdown in situational awareness. The most widely used example of this in crew resource management training is the Tenerife disaster of 1977. They were ranked to this day as the worst aviation disaster of all time with 583 people killed after two Jumbo 747 jets collided on a fog-bound runway. Like nearly all significant accidents, there were many contributing factors that led to the disaster, some relating to situational awareness. The leading cause was one of the captains took off without clearance while another jumbo was still on the runway.

Before we look at how we lose situational awareness, we must first understand what it is. There are many extended definitions in many different texts and a variety of information across the internet; however, I prefer the UK's Health and Safety Executives definition as it is simplistic and to the point:

*Situational Awareness is being aware of what is happening around you in terms of where you are, where you're supposed to be and whether anyone or anything around you is a threat to your health or safety.*

There are a lot of elements that formulate a person's situational awareness. You must be aware of time, your location and the location of others. As an aviation instructor, I used to tell my students that they can be the best crewman, pilot or navigator in the world but the one who will kill you is the idiot in the wrong place at the wrong time.

That statement rang true when I was under training with MICA paramedics in central Melbourne, Australia. As part of my medical training as an aircrew officer on a SAR flight, I observed helping out these advanced paramedics in a single responder vehicle. We would be called to an incident or emergency in the middle of the city and would need to get there fast with the lights flashing and sirens blaring. I realised how crucial their situational awareness was when we approached a crossroad and would slow right down to check traffic had stopped in response to the siren and lights. They knew the streets like the backs of their hands but they also knew the details given by dispatch—what the job was and, in particular, what constituted an urgent job. Professionals have to be very conscious of what is going on around them in every element of their situation.

Often in major incidents or accidents, the leading contributory cause is a breakdown in situational awareness by the person at the centre of the incident or the overall person in charge of the incident.

The most common factor for losing situational awareness is a distraction. I often describe this as the noise of modern life and, in particular, modern communications. Distractions are several things: emails, text messages, phone calls or can even be a breakdown in communications, being task-focused or simply losing track of time. When teaching, I often like to begin a discussion with the question 'What professions are good at situational awareness?'

In society and industry, there are many professions, such as air traffic controllers and teachers but my favourite example is chefs. It's a great example because we have all attempted to cook a meal for someone else or at least most of us have dabbled in catering, even if it's just a roast dinner for our friends or family.

There are many factors to cooking in a meal, such as different ingredient cooking times, keeping things warm and serving everything up at the right time. Then we add taste to the situation and you have so many different flavours to contend with too much or too little can ruin a meal. Anyone who has children will also know that there is an added pressure of getting the children's meals out on time. Children are far less forgiving than adults and they will cause mayhem in a restaurant if they don't get their food. The thing with human factors is that it all comes together; communication, leadership, teamwork, to name a few of the elements. Situational awareness is a combination of all the human non-technical skills working together.

I would like to take the liberty to relay a personal tale of mine. It is one of a few occasions in my life where I felt that I was close to having a fatal accident and a great example of how lack of situational awareness can cause accidents. What worried me afterwards was I just seemed to miss the warning signs. I was a licensed crew resource management instructor and yet even though I taught aircrews to watch out for all the warning signs that I failed to see myself—let alone act on them.

One of the factors that dropped my defences was that this particular flight was my last before moving on to new pastures with the company. It was a winter's day in Shetland and it was snowy. Unusual in Shetland because of the warm gulf-stream that flowed past the islands made it rare to snow on the islands. As I drove to work, I was slightly excited as I had a great crew to work with for my last shift.

I wandered into work like a well-oiled machine, navigating through the handover before gathering in the operations room to hear the captain's brief on our next 24 hours.

The context of this case refers to something previously discussed, which is "perceived pressure". The captain was determined to achieve a specific task—night deck winching. He was going on leave and if he did not fill his currency for night winching to a vessel during the shift, he would be out of date for this currency on his return from leave. Under the rules, this would involve extra flights and roster issues, which as a trainer himself, the captain intended to avoid by completing the currency during the shift. He had done all the right things: checked the weather, arranged a vessel and prepared a brief for his crew.

We sat in the operations room and the captain gave us a comprehensive brief on what he would like to achieve during our shift, which was mainly the night deck winching to a vessel. He informed us that the weather was terrible for the first part of our shift. However, it should improve and be within training limits as we started the night-time portion.

As my last shift on this base, the day went quickly; I was busy organising a move south and an eventual move to Holland. Before I knew it, dinner had arrived and we gathered in the crew room to eat our evening meal. I then noticed that the wintry picture outside the window had not changed much during the day. We gathered for a brief in the operations room and the captain talked us through the flight profile and assigned us all jobs. The weather was as briefed within the training limitations for night flying.

Winter in Shetland is pretty bleak; however, it does have a strange sort of beauty to it. That aside, I donned my thermals and a suit called a "woolly bear"—it may be pretty outside but it was also pretty cold. Warm clothing and a survival suit were mandatory. Then over the top, a life jacket and associated survival aids within each life jacket side pocket—finally, a neck warmer and my flying helmet with a thermal skullcap. I felt bulky and cumbersome as I walked out to the aircraft.

The snowflakes were still falling as we approached the aircraft, covered in a thin white blanket of snow particles that seemed to stick to the aircraft's shell before melting away. I climbed into the helicopter via the air-stair door and made my way forward to the winch operator's crew position. The captain and co-pilot went through the checklist and then asked if we were ready to start in the cabin. We acknowledged that indeed we were prepared and the captain pressed the start button. The aircraft's number two engine started as it was the 18th of the month, an even-numbered day, odd days such as the 11th would constitute a start of number one engine. This a standard procedure to ensure the engines are used equally for a start.

I conducted my checks of the hoist, set up the GPS navigation unit at my station and checked in with the coastguard on the radio. All standard; no surprises, everything was going to plan. We would be conducting our night winching to the coastguard tug, leaving Scallaway Harbour, a small town about 30 to 40 miles away. I could not talk to the vessel yet as I was on the ground and there was a lot of high ground between us. As we taxied away from the coastguard helicopter hanger to the take-off point, I noticed that the weather was getting worse, which made me think to talk with the vessel and ask how their weather fared as soon as the post-take-off checks completed.

All the initial checks completed and we headed down Sumburgh's north taxiway to join the westerly runway for a take-off to the west. The snow showers began to worsen and the pilots changed their departure brief five times to air traffic. The pilot's reason they changed their departure request was the changes in visibility due to the snow, forcing them between a visual departure and an instrument departure. The frustration was showing from the voice of the air traffic controller, who in the end simply stated that we could depart any way we wished.

I must admit feeling reserved about the flight at this point; the changes in departure type was an obvious warning sign that our subconscious had picked up. The captain's confident manner, his vast experience and assertiveness that the weather remained within limits masked these warning signs, which as a crew and individuals, we choose to ignore.

Up, we climbed into the blackness of the Shetland night and the continuing snow showers. We had an initial transit dead ahead for around 10 minutes to avoid some high ground on our right and then we would turn with a northerly heading to rendezvous with the vessel.

We completed the after-take-off checks and I talked to the coastguard control centre in Lerwick, the capital of Shetland.

They confirmed the vessel had sailed and the working frequency it would be on. I contacted the ship and established communications. The next step was to ask for their position and current weather situation; I unconsciously added the question, 'Are you in snow showers?'

The chap on the other end relayed his position, the local weather and told me, 'No, there's no snow showers out here.' On hearing this message from the vessel, the aircraft captain stated,

"See, I told you these are just showers and it is clearing up". Yet something in the tug crewman's voice made me think that he was not a person who knew what to look for in a weather report. He was possibly a deckhand, lookout or an ordinary seaman and had not received any formal training in meteorology.

We continued on our way and made the turn north towards the ship's position that the ship provided via radio. As I looked through my bubble window, I noticed ice building up on the turret that contained the forward-looking infra-red (FLIR) camera. It seemed it was still snowing and I was feeling quite uncomfortable with the whole situation.

I then peered forward into the cockpit at the multi-function display panel, looking for the weather RADAR display. The screen situated between both the pilots on the main instrument panel. It is rectangular in shape with a modern screen, found in what is an otherwise analogue cockpit. The visual paint (the area in front of the aircraft that the RADAR examines) on the screen spans approximately 90°, so 45° on either side of the aircraft's dead ahead.

I looked for bright red on the screen, indicating a level three radar return and any associated level two (yellow) or level one (green) returns. Level three returns show heavy precipitation; possibly leading to thunderstorms; this was something to be wary of as turbulence and hail are also associated with thunderstorms. I was surprised at what I saw when I looked at the screen. 30 degrees on either side of the aircraft's heading was reading blank with a touch of yellow and green at 40° on either side and only red on the periphery. The lack of red seemed strange to me as it meant there were no weather bands ahead and yet looking through my window, I could see heavy snowfall.

We continued and the feelings of uncertainty began to truly grip me like a vice slowly entrapping me in its jaws. I looked out of my bubble window again and noticed more ice accreting on the FLIR turret and called the ship once more.

This time, I was clearly speaking to the master of the vessel and when I enquired about the weather, in particular, whether there were any snow showers, he immediately answered. He told us that they were in a giant snow shower and they were getting a lot of settling snow on his vessel.

The aircraft captain was listening in on the radio conversation and said straight away, 'Okay, this is getting silly, let's cancel and go home to base,' or words to that effect. I can't honestly say I took much notice of his words so much as the tone of resignation in his voice, as he said, 'Let's go home,' which is all I wanted to hear. I called the tug master and cancelled, thanking him and his crew for their assistance and apologising for the wasted trip. I think he was pretty glad to be returning to port in this wintery Shetland weather.

Until that point, I would say our situational awareness had been pretty good or so we thought. I had kept a plot on a map of our position relative to the high ground around us. I was sure the pilots were happy with their situational awareness; however, there were some significant things occurring with the aircraft that we did not know of at the time. These things would prove to be potentially catastrophic for us in a short while.

The pilots turned us 180° and we started south again. Aware of the headland to our left as was the winchman, who had also been keeping a navigational plot. The co-pilot was flying the aircraft and the captain was managing the flight and talking on the radio. He called Sumburgh tower and informed them that we were returning for a visual approach to runway 09.

The air traffic controller informed us that she had fixed-wing traffic lining up to make an Instrument Landing System (ILS) approach on runway two-seven at around 40 miles; we were to report at ten nautical miles from the field. At this point, things started to get interesting. We had no visual clues that we were clear of the high ground to the west and north of the airfield. Usually, you could see the village of Toab, which is slightly to the north of the airport, and if you kept left somewhat, the runway would be dead ahead.

The pilots completed some checks and there was discussion in the cockpit regarding the approach and landing. The wind was westerly and our groundspeed was a bit faster than anticipated.

At this point, lights appeared visually ahead and the captain asked the co-pilot if he had eyes on the runway. The co-pilot said that he could not see it and I looked forward through the window to find that I could not see any runway or light either. This discussion seemed to go on for a while and as the captain stated that he could see clearly, he became frustrated that the co-pilot couldn't see the runway or its lights. Eventually, the captain said that he would handle the approach as he had the runway sighted.

He took control and within what seemed an incredibly short time, we were over the airfield. At this point, it got stimulating; it appeared the entire front of the aircraft had impacted snow on it, around a couple of centimetres thick. The pilot's only view was through a small gap that the wipers were struggling to keep clear. The controller in the tower became a little frantic and quite angry as she saw a colossal helicopter appear out of nowhere from the west. She knew a fixed-wing was incredibly close to landing from the opposite direction and was very conscious of the two aircraft getting perilously close to each other.

I was aware that the pilot had minimal hover references because of the ice and immediately left my seat to open the sliding door behind the captain to assist him with an almost rally-driver patter to get us onto the ground.

We landed into wind on the northern taxiway and returned to base. To be honest, I was a little shaken. I remember getting out of the aircraft and looking back at it as the pilots shut the rotors down; vast blocks of ice flew off in chunks from the blades and rotor head. Safely inside the hanger, the captain called the tower and apologised for the unorthodox approach and then we all sat down and debriefed this relatively short and interesting flight.

For some clarity there are a couple of reasons why the air traffic controller had no idea where we were. Firstly, we had missed the ten nautical mile call requested by ATC due to the conversations on how we would complete the approach. To exacerbate this, we had not noted that we were downwind and as the wind speed was around an average of 45 to 60 knots, we were travelling faster than perceived. We effectively were travelling at times around 180 knots across the ground, that's 91 metres every second; hence we ran out of time.

Secondly, the tower had experienced the exact heavy snowfall on her windows, so the western facing windows were obscured entirely by impacted snow. It is not surprising she would have been quite startled by this rather large helicopter suddenly appearing next to her as a fixed-wing was coming from the other direction.

If we break this down now into elements of situational awareness, we can see that we lost some attention. I say we because any one of us could have intervened and cancelled the flight before further issues or threats to the training mission occurred.

Elements of situational awareness:

1. We misjudged the weather and the significance of weather report reliability. A warning to the crew would have been the five changes during the departure brief to ATC.
2. We failed to realise how much ice and snow had built up on the aircraft. Although I had seen ice and snow on the FLIR turret and reported it to the rest of the crew.
3. We failed to make the ten nautical mile call to the ATC, which would have given them an awareness of our position relative to the airfield and the approaching traffic.
4. We failed to notice the rapidly closing distance between us and the airfield.

I learned lots of valuable lessons with this flight; it was the classic example of how human factors affect judgement. There were so many points during the flight where the flight should have been cancelled early. It rings true each time I teach human factors how all the minor elements can line up against you.

Human factor elements:

1. The captain had perceived pressure to get his night deck currency in.
2. The weather forecast and actual weather were significantly different. On that point, the captain could have been making lulls in the snow showers to fit the forecast weather.
3. The crew's reluctance to be assertive and speak up about the weather, even though the signs were there.
4. ATC's reluctance to question the many changes in departure and the crew's reluctance to be assertive with these changes. (Is it essential to continue if the flight crew changed the flight rules for departure five times?)
5. The whole crew's situational awareness of the approaching aircraft arriving at a similar time from the opposite direction.

A principle of human factors is that a combination of all the elements is needed to achieve competency. Each principle interlinks; without communication, we can't accomplish any other human factor element. In situational awareness, communication is fundamental in decision making. How can we make the right decision if we are not aware of all the variables, such as time, location and all other elements? It was a training mission, that's all. There is some merit in the argument to train in the conditions you fly your missions. However, do you need almost to die trying?

As said at the beginning of the chapter, a great example of a professional with great situational awareness is the kitchen's head chef. They have to think of many variables during the cooking of a meal. Then make decisions based on what has happened, what is happening now and what will be happening. They must then relate all this information to achieve an end goal—getting the food to the customer.

I have constructed a task management model that provides a method of effectively managing a task. It utilises a decision-making tool I developed called LIFE, which allows the team leader to logically look at how to make decisions when given a job. The critical element to situational awareness is feedback from your team throughout the task.

**Life:**

1. **Look** for solutions.
2. **Investigate** all options – encourage ideas from your team.
3. **Find** a solution.
4. **Evaluate** outcomes.

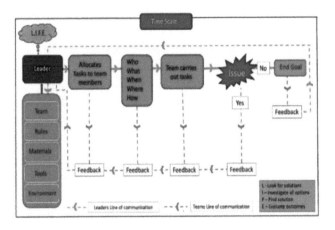

**Figure 4a**

First, the leader accepts a task and then establishes a timeline to achieve the mission.

The leader will then establish:

- The team.
- The rules in place, such as boundaries, time limits and safety limitations.
- What materials are available and need to be to achieve the task.
- The tools available to achieve the task, such as transport and equipment to lift things.
- The environment where the task will take place, such as weather and location.

Once he has gathered all the initial information, he uses the LIFE decision-making tool. A good leader will find a solution; however, a good leader must also request feedback and encourage suggestions from the team.

A leader needs to provide their team with who, what, when, where and how to complete their allocated task. The leader then allows the team to carry out their roles and functions. The leader should continue to use LIFE throughout the task's progression.

If an issue occurs, the leader is informed through feedback, returns to the LIFE model for a solution and repeats the process. If there are no issues, the team completes the task and provides feedback upon completion. The leader must return input to the team at the end.

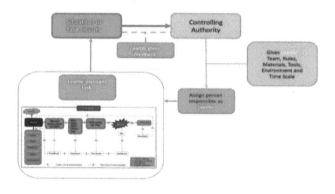

**Figure 4b**

The task management model (Figure 4b) relates to tasks where there is a bigger picture. Someone has to be the controlling authority to coordinate and allocate tasks and this could be a police control room or a national rescue coordination centre. They will delegate the job to a leader but importantly, they too must receive feedback from their designated leader to maintain situational awareness.

If things are not going well, the controlling authority can pass the leadership role to someone new. The previous leader can either step down a level and manage sub-tasks or leave the situation. The important thing is they must hand over recent feedback from their team to the new leader.

Let's look at this model with an emergency response scenario to an emergency, such as a road accident. The first thing to establish is who is the leader and who is legally responsible.

Consider a multiple car pile-up on a major road. The control room supervisor will delegate the task to an on-scene commander. It usually is the first unit on the scene in most countries until an established or trained leader has arrived.

The initial task leader will establish what timescale he or she has, then report any rules that may affect the task. Say the situation is a bad car crash, the teams will be the fire department, police and medical. They must then work out what materials and tools are required and finally, what environmental issues there are.

In this situation, each team leader for the respective service that attends the scene establishes their own needs, i.e. team, rules, materials, tools and environment. They will provide feedback to the task leader as to their resources and capabilities. The task leader then takes a few minutes to go through the LIFE decision model to seek input and ideas from each services team leader.

Afterwards, they will allocate the tasks that need completion, ensuring that they know who, when, what, where and how each service leader completes their tasks. They must establish good communication and request feedback.

Let's examine one of the services: the fire service.

**Who**: Fire service team leader.

**When**: As quickly as possible.

**What**: Ensure the team secures the scene and it is safe from hazards of fire and explosion.

**Where**: The immediate area of the accident and a radius of 50 metres in all directions.

**How**: Following standard operating procedures and safety management systems, utilising specialised equipment and vehicles.

The fire service team leader will utilise their task management model to carry out the task. If there are any issues, such as insufficient human resources, they must report back to the overall task leader. The overall leader will consider LIFE again and may allocate some policemen to assist the fire service.

Once the task is complete, the fire service leader reports back to the overall task leader. The overall leader must give the fire service leader feedback to keep them focused as there may be additional tasks. An example would be something like, 'Good job, you got that achieved quickly and safely, we can now send the medical teams in for assessments and start recovery.' Even if there are no more tasks, it is always good to give feedback and it builds morale, keeps teams motivated and develops goodwill.

The overall team leader can pass feedback back up to the controlling authority, who assists them with their situational awareness on how the incident is developing.

In almost any situation, you can use this model to task manage a team. Take a medical team conducting a surgical procedure, where the hospital allocates a time slot for the operation and a timescale to achieve it. The hospital then assigns a surgical leader to perform the leadership function to accomplish the task.

The surgical leader then allocates tasks as the operation progresses and requests feedback from their team to maintain situational awareness of how the process is moving. Once the operation completes, the job is handed over to the appropriate personnel, who will take over the patient's safety and wellbeing.

Like all aspects of human factors, situational awareness intermeshes with all the other abilities required. You cannot achieve tasks if you have poor communication, become too task-focused or fail to ask or receive feedback.

Loss of situational awareness is one of the most common causes of accidents and incidents and usually is one of the last links in the chain before a catastrophe. A common thread in aircraft accident reports is the captain having a minor emergency but failing to manage it and snowballing into a major crisis.

Often this is because the captain continued to fly the aircraft and tried to manage the emergency himself, losing situational awareness from overloading his decision-making capacity. In other walks of life, it is much the same. The surgeon becomes unaware of what is happening with the patient during an operation or the tired driver loses concentration and drives down a one-way street.

Incidents are always a result of failing in many human-factor competencies. Communication is the main culprit, followed by distraction with a smattering of mental bias and health issues, impacting overall situational awareness. Hence, it is crucial to maintain situational awareness throughout our lives, especially in aviation and emergency service.

# Chapter 5
# Communication

Communication is an interregnal part of our everyday lives. It is often down to poor communication when we fail, despite it being a straightforward concept. In its most basic form, you only need three things for communication: a transmitter, message and receiver. So, where do we go wrong? One of the reasons could be noise. In communication noise is the general background distractions caused by social, physical and mental issues.

**Figure 5a**

There are two elements to communication, which are:

1. Verbal
2. Non-Verbal

## Verbal

Although verbal communication seems straight forward, some visual stimuli affect verbal communication, such as body language. Below is a chart that displays how body language makes up 55% of verbal communication effectiveness.

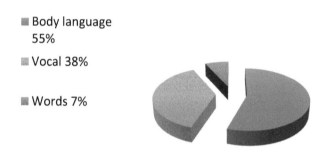

**Figure 5b**

The vocal element comprises many things: how fast we speak, the tone of our voice and our voice volume. When I asked people to describe a good "telling off" by a boss or parent, they claim the people who best dispatch a damn good telling off never raise their voices. Why is this? Perhaps a person who rants and raves only exhibits a loss of control in the situation.

Words are still important, although it is only responsible for 7% of the effectiveness. A sharp repartee or banter can be very effective; Oscar Wilde was a master of this, 'Some cause happiness wherever they go; others when they go.' An excellent example of his sharp wit.

I often wonder while holding conversations with the younger generation of today, why must they insist on putting "like" at the end of every other word? It is most annoying listening to, as seen here:

*She was like really annoying, Dad, like really annoying and was like calling me names and like coming in my bedroom and everything.*

It has almost become the norm to add the word "like" to every other. I am amazed at how many so-called professionals seem to have developed this trait of "likeness".

Using all of these elements in figure 11a can be very effective and a good orator will combine all of these elements to transmit their message. Who first comes to mind when you think of a good speaker? My personal favourites are Winston Churchill, JF Kennedy and Barrack Obama. All three use words effectively but they also combine this with effective body language and vocal communication. JFK and Barrack Obama use their hands to emphasise their point in a very open and engaging manner. Churchill would start a speech with his hands clenched before him and as the address gained momentum, he would place his hands on his hips. Successful speakers often combine humour in their speeches, although not everyone is a natural comedian and humour should be used with caution.

## Non-verbal

This technological age provides many variations on how to communicate. Phones, fax machines, pagers, radio, television, the list seems endless. If we look at the animal kingdom, we can see how animals, even the simplest of organisms, get around communication barriers by all manner of means. Including using chemicals such as pheromones to mark territory or take bees, who release a chemical to warn other colony members that they are under attack. The use of colour in the natural world is also effective. Cuttlefish and octopi can display mood by changing colour; they flash bright colours as a sign of danger to predators. A great example is the tiny blue-ringed octopus, who flashes vivid blue circles as a warning to avoid its highly poisonous bite.

When I first joined the navy in the late 1970s, personal mobile communication devices did not exist, telephoning from overseas was expensive and letter writing was the way to go. Often it would be weeks before letters from home would reach you. This could be problematic as if sometimes the letters would take different routes to home, causing letters to arrive out of sync. If you read letters out of order, then any messages within the letter content may be seen or become entirely out of context. I have seen many a relationship become strained over a letter. We fixed this problem by numbering letters when we sent them and the first letter would be number one and so on.

Nowadays, we are in the realm of instant communication. We started with just voice messaging and now we can effectively video conference with software such as Skype, FaceTime and Messenger. Thanks to smartphones and the Internet, voice, words and body language can all come into play.

However, in some professions and circumstances, there are still barriers. The surgical team may have to wear surgical masks to prevent infection (see Figure 11b) or the search and rescue team on a rescue helicopter, who wear helmets and safety equipment that means they cannot see each other (see Figure 11c). These people lose some effectiveness in their communication due to their reduced body language elements.

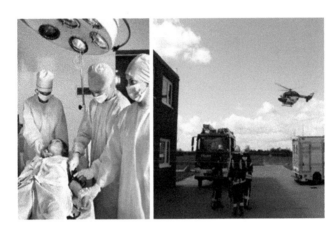

**Figure 5c**                    **Figure 5d**

Humans are good at overcoming restrictions in many communication elements. Say two people speak different languages and it is incredible to watch how they overcome their lack of words and rely on body language and vocal elements. However, a friend and his foreign girlfriend visited us, communicating via a translation app on their phones. It is funny how in western cultures the lack of language skills sometimes causes us to turn the volume up and speak slower when communicating with a foreigner.

Sign language is another good example, people with hearing loss or impairment use body language and signing very effectively. Young people in noisy night clubs also seem pretty capable of communicating without the ability to listen to each other. So, what barriers to effective communication do we have? (See Table 5).

| Body language | Verbal | Words |
| --- | --- | --- |
| Protective clothing | Background noise | Language |
| Distance | Volume control | Culture |
| Bad visibility | Time | Homonyms |
| Physical disability | Hearing disability | Different pronunciation |
| Day or night | Tone of voice | Inflection |
| Physical Location | | |
| Eye contact | | |

**Table 5a**

With all these barriers, it is easy to see why humans can be so bad at communication in verbal elements. If we break these down further, we can see the gritty reality of why we can be so bad at communication. Culture can play a significant part in the various communication barriers. In Asian and African cultures, the need to save face can be so strong, they will either not talk to you at all or simply lie to avoid the confrontation of talking through an issue.

I know a training captain once recalled a time he was teaching Asian students about engine failures in an aeroplane simulator. After giving the students a brief on the impending simulated engine failure and confirming if the student had any questions, the immediate reply was they understood everything. To the amazement of the training captain when the engine failure was instigated, the reaction from the students was absolutely nothing. The training captain repeated his brief and instructions for the co-pilot (the student) to perform and then reset the simulator. Again, the engine failure was instigated and once more a complete non-reaction from the Asian co-pilot.

The training captain soon discovered that the fundamental English skills needed comprehend the instructions simply was not there. However, the Asian student did not wish to relay this information to the training captain, making them lose face in front of a European. The cultural instinct was so strong that I don't want to imagine what may have happened if discovered during an actual flight and not a simulation.

The flip side to this is the complete opposite of the Asian face-saving culture—western cultures are upfront and say it like it is. Scandinavians can sometimes be perceived as abrupt in the way they convey the very basics of their message. When I worked in Norway over the winter months some years ago, I found this Scandinavian trait quite amusing. I was told that if you say to a Norwegian 'I am cold,' they will immediately inform you, 'You are not cold; you are simply wearing inadequate clothing.' The simplicity of the message is brilliant and perhaps we could all learn from this and refer back to simplistic language to convey our messages.

In western cultures, lack of communication can often come down to simple embarrassment. The transmitting person feels uncomfortable or is afraid of the responsive reaction from the person receiving their information. The quality of moral courage is one of the fundamental requirements of good leadership and management. It is also a pillar of effective communication—we sometimes need to tell people what they don't want to hear. Any parent will tell you that telling a young child it is time for bed, especially if granny and granddad are there, is often met with a very adverse reaction from the said child. A robust and assertive response to the negativity needs to be given to save the situation.

To be an effective communicator, you need to have the courage sometimes to say it as it is. The delivery of the message is the key, although there are no hard and fast rules other than when bad news needs to be given and is best done in person. Just be prepared for the reaction of the receiver to your message. No one likes to be given bad news by non-personal contact and I think everyone has heard of someone being fired over the phone or, worse, being informed by text or email. The transmitter has lacked the courage to tell the person directly because they are afraid of the reaction; it is both cowardly and cruel.

Eye contact can be challenging for some people. I had a survival instructor in the navy who simply could not look people in the eye. He would give his lectures or lessons and be staring at some point way in the distance, high above the audience's heads. He did not strike me as a timid person but put him in front of a class and he simply could not look at anybody in the eye. I found it a bit off-putting and I think his message could have been lost to some. Good use of eye contact is an excellent way to engage an audience.

Steve Jobs, the late boss of Apple, constantly engaged his audience. He had a relaxed manner and through clever use of eye contact, he could convey his message through both the camera and with the people directly in the audience. It almost felt as if he talked explicitly to you, even though you may have been thousands of miles away watching him on your computer or television.

The amount of time you look someone in the eye is important too. A politician or a presenter will sweep the room while talking; this engages everyone in a general manner. In comparison, a police officer or a salesperson will give each person a positive glance directly focused on individuals.

Body language can be a powerful tool in communication; you only have to look at a politician giving a press conference to witness careful use of body language. Tony Blair, former UK Prime Minister, was very good at this. Blair used his hands when talking to display openness and honesty.

Body language can also be used negatively. You can be sure of a person's displeasure towards you from the body language they use. The "cold shoulder" is often used to describe this disagreeable body language, outstanding examples being closed gestures such as folded arms or crossed legs. Note the body language in Figures 11d and e.

**Figure 5e**                **Figure 5f**

The first says 'I'm not happy' through subtle messages in body language. By looking at the picture in Figure 11d, you can see that they have bland unsmiling expressions. They are not looking at the camera or each other and thus have no direct eye contact. The woman has her arms crossed and the man has his hands in his pockets; these are closed gestures like barriers between the receiver and themselves. This body language is giving us a clear but subliminal message: we are not happy.

The opposite is seen in Figure 11e: open arms, smiles and direct eye contact with the camera. There are no barriers between the receiver and the transmitters and it is a direct message that they are happy and wish to convey this to you, the receiver of the message.

Have you ever met someone and just minutes later could not remember their name? A medical friend of mine told me that the reason for this. It is because 60% of your brain is trying to figure out if that person is a threat to you. I'm not sure if this is true but it seems plausible.

When I was at the Britannia Naval College, significant importance is placed on social skills. I brought this observation up with a tutor, who discussed this with the rest of the students. He noticed that when he had met American Naval Officers, they repeated a person's name back to them when they initially met. I am still not convinced this method works; however, it may be a helpful tool for some.

In all aspects of working or private life, we must practice the art of communication. It is something I find myself working on constantly, particularly in my personal life. At work, you may be forced to be a good communicator as part of being a striving professional and being recognised for your work. However, at home, we tend to let it slip or, in my case, simply let it go entirely on occasion.

When we are comfortable with someone, we relax too much and the art of communication becomes slightly less important. I know we have all seen an elderly couple in a restaurant or pub and observed how they just sit opposite each other in complete silence. Not one word is uttered other than to respond to the odd anecdote between them. Perhaps they don't need to communicate because they have developed a relationship over many years and just simple conversation is all that is necessary? I don't know the true answer to that, but I know that many relationship break-ups are caused by poor communication.

A large part of communication is the ability to listen. My favourite phrase from when my youngest daughter was a teenager, 'You have two ears and one mouth, please use them in that ratio.'

Feedback is a word I hear a lot in human-factors courses. Feedback is an excellent medium for developing good working relationships. How do we know we are working well if we do not receive feedback? With that said, this can be difficult for a variety of reasons. As humans, we generally don't like to receive negative information. In the courses I've taught, I have developed a methodology that feedback is a good thing—even when perceived negatively.

A common thing in most courses nowadays is to complete a survey, questionnaire or feedback form upon finishing a course. If you look at anything you do in life, we need to determine if what we are doing is correct or can be improved. Or even more important, are we doing anything wrong? A few times in this book, I have stated that people in accidents don't realise they are making mistakes or doing something wrong; this is why feedback is so important.

I reviewed an accident report on Flight BA5390, a high-profile accident in England in 1990. It was so high-profile that one of the consequences of the accident was the windscreen failing and the captain of the flight was sucked out his window due to the window securing bolts failing. The quick actions of the crew saved his life.

As I was looking through the report, a statement jumped out at me, 'The store's supervisor, who had been in the job for about 16 years, informed him that A211-8Ds were used to fit that windscreen, but did not press the point.'

The windscreen failed for many reasons, one of which was incorrect bolts being fitted. An excellent example of assertive communication; if the experienced store's supervisor had been more assertive, the engineer might have obtained the correct size bolts. When you read accident reports, you soon pick up on common scenarios that occur and non-assertive communication is a common thread.

Often it occurs with what we call the "cockpit gradient" (Figure 5f); this is when you have a senior captain and a junior co-pilot. In this case, we say that the gradient slope would be steep and heavily weighted towards the captain. If you have two senior captains or a more senior co-pilot, the slope is more level.

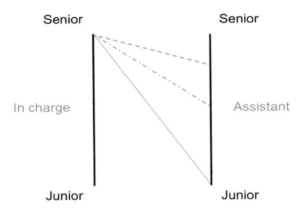

**Figure 5g**
The Seniority Gradient

This gradient applies to all occupations and industries—a person in charge and an assistant or employee. As a rule of thumb, it is difficult to tell a senior figure in the company that what they are doing is wrong, mainly when you are junior to them.

In the diagram, you see that the more senior the assistant, the gradient starts to flatten. Although the gradient will never be level unless they are of equal standing. Generally, communication becomes more accessible as the slope flattens.

When both are of equal standing, someone has to be in charge and responsible for the task outcome. When this is not clear, it causes all sorts of problems and can lead to an even more dangerous situation. I have seen this when two training captains fly together and it is complicated for a training captain to tell another training captain that they are making a mistake. It can also be dangerous if they become complacent and unaware of the other pilot's actions. As they are still trainees, their guard drops when they are flying with equally experienced pilots.

I came across this when I worked in the North Sea and an incident occurred during night-currency deck training. Night currency is simply training to ensure you have the appropriate experience to cope with the rigours of flying in the dark and the added difficulties of landing on a deck at night.

The aircraft was a helicopter that was practising deck landings on an oil-rig helicopter landing deck. The two pilots were very experienced and as it was a SAR helicopter, they carried the helicopter's technical crew. The initial flight and landings went as expected and everyone settled into the procedures. However, during one of the approaches, the deck crew and one of the technical crew noticed they were about to land with the undercarriage in the up position. The aircraft did an immediate climb and aborted the landing.

How could this happen with two very experienced pilots? I remember reading the company report and the exact details of the report findings are a little vague now, so it would be unfair to speculate on what went wrong. My point, however, is to show that accidents and incidents can occur to even the most experienced crews.

In each different industry, we have these gradients. Sometimes it can be between occupations of the same sector: the surgeon and the anaesthetist, the engineer and the store man, a ship officer and a seaman, a scientist and an engineer. The relationship between characters Howard and Shelden in the "The Big Bang Theory" television show displays this relationship between different professionals very comically and aptly expressed. Sheldon's character often dismisses Howard's ideas simply because he does not have a doctorate and is not a "true" scientist but an engineer.

As a species, we need to move beyond these gradients and when we sense something is not right, be assertive and communicate the fact. It may well save our lives and others that we may directly control. I am amazed when reading accident reports that people understand the situation is rapidly escalating towards imminent danger but still fail to communicate this vital information.

I confess I need to work a lot on my communications skills in everyday life. Perhaps we should all try a little harder to actually talk to each other rather than rely entirely on non-verbal communication, such as text or email. Without communication, all the other non-technical skills in human factors or team resource management are ineffective. It is, therefore, a core skill for a significant reason.

# Chapter 6
# Accidents and Incidents

Accidents and incidents definitions can be found in most operation manuals and safety management systems. They are a fact of life; every day, there are literally hundreds of thousands of accidents—in the workplace, at home, on the road. The consequences vary from a tragic loss of life to insignificant minor injuries. They can be caused by bizarre and unusual circumstances or deliberate and intentional acts that become catalysts for an accident.

The definition of an accident:

*An unfortunate incident that happens unexpectedly and* ***unintentionally****, typically resulting in damage or injury.*

I have highlighted the word unintentionally for a good reason as I have said many times already. We may try hard to prevent accidents with health and safety programs, safety management systems, risk assessments and threat and error management but we cannot stop them entirely.

A common phrase used to describe individuals prone to accidents is "clumsiness". Subjectively, there is some doubt over the validity that some people are more prone to accidents than others. A well-known group blamed for accidents by the general public is young male drivers. There is a presumption that young male drivers statistically have a higher proportion of traffic accidents than other groups, such as drivers over 45.

Like any statistic, the interpretation of numbers is interpolated in many ways. I researched road deaths in the state of Victoria from February 2015–16. The figures were interesting; below is a chart showing fatalities by age group.

The yearly total of traffic accidents up to the end of February 2016 was 245 with 263 fatalities. The chart shows that you are far more likely to die in an accident the older you are. The peaks appear to be between 18–20 and, strangely, 40–49. The ratio of male VS female fatalities was 188 male casualties compared to 75 females.

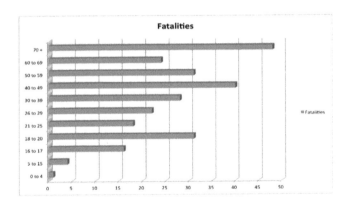

**Table 6a**

Fatalities in the state of Victoria by age group.

Table 6b shows injuries requiring hospital treatment (based on claims data) relating to these accidents. The data reveals that as we get older, we are more likely to be injured.

Statistics can be manipulated as anybody watching a political debate during election campaigns can testify.

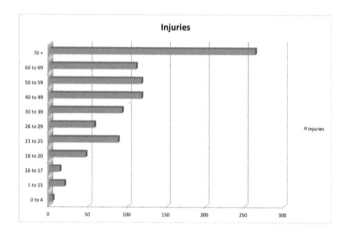

**Table 6b**

The number of injuries resulting in claimed hospital care.

Additional nationwide evidence shows 40%-45% per year of young Australian deaths from injury is due to traffic accidents. If we look at the statistics between 16–25-year-olds in Table 6a, the total number of deaths is 65, which is just over a fifth of the total in the whole state of Victoria. Furthermore, the percentage increases when you consider that this age group only represents between 15–20% of the total license holders in the state.

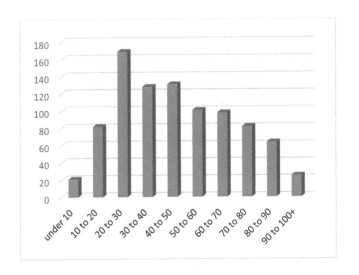

**Table 6c**

Road deaths in Australia by age group 1/1/2017 until 30/9/2017

Therefore, in my interpolation of this data—yes, young drivers seem to be involved in more accidents and, furthermore, a ratio of 3:1 male to female. In the latest information at the time of editing the book (Nov 2017) shown in table 6c, the 20 to 30-year-olds have the highest fatality rate at 18.7% of the 900 deaths to date.

While traffic accident investigation is conducted thoroughly, it is not always in the public domain and not as strictly governed as other accident investigation forms. One industry where the accident cause is vigorously pursued is the aviation industry.

Without a doubt, there is more accident data from aircraft accidents than any other. Although police traffic investigation teams examine accidents, the sources of data are limited. Aircraft investigators, however, have much more data to call upon, including air traffic tape recordings, radar data, black boxes with cockpit voice recordings, aircraft performance data, and access to pilot and engineering records.

An excellent example of an aircraft accident investigation is Bergenair Flight 301. The tragic accident demonstrates many elements of improper crew resource management and mental bias and error chains.

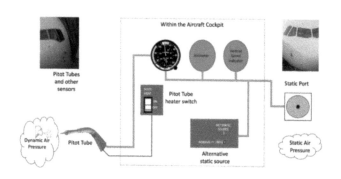

**Figure 6d**
A basic pitot-static system in an aircraft.

Bergenair was a small charter company that had run into financial difficulties, which forced them to cut costs. The doomed aircraft was due for repairs and had been left on the ground for 20 days in Puerto Plata, Dominican Republic. Aircraft, when not flying, have covers fitted over any equipment or engine intakes to prevent objects falling in or animals entering vital systems. This aircraft was left unattended with the covers for the pitot tubes removed for a period of two to three days before the fateful flight.

A pitot tube is a small hollow metallic tube located on the nose of an aeroplane, its purpose is to measure airspeed and it does so by allowing air to pass through and into the pitot-static system (see Figure 6d).

The pitot-static system provides information to many instruments in the cockpit, including pressure information by static or dynamic air entering the pitot tube and static vents. Dynamic air or pressure occurs when air is forced into the pitot tube dynamically as the aircraft travels through the air. Static air, in simplistic terms, is the air around us, the pressure of this air changes frequently. The static port measures the pressure of this air and displays this on the cockpit instruments.

The instruments use the pitot-static system to provide speed, height, rate of climb and descent information through an analogue aircraft or a primary flight display in a modern glass cockpit. This system played a relatively minor role in the accident but a significant part in managing the error chain, which eventually led to the crash.

Returning to the accident, as mentioned, the aircraft had been on the ground for some time. Berginair had a larger aircraft scheduled for a flight to Frankfurt via some stopovers but the company deemed there were not enough passengers for the larger aircraft. It decided to organise the Boeing 757 instead and at short notice had the aircraft and crew prepare the flight.

The captain was one of the most senior in the company with 24 750 flying hours. His co-pilot had 3 500 hours, inexperienced in comparison; however, a relief pilot was also in the cockpit. The relief pilot was also a captain and had 15 000 hours of flying experience, not an insignificant amount of flying.

The initial checks and taxi to the runway were conducted without any irregularities. The first hint of trouble was 17 seconds into the take-off run, the captain reported, 'My airspeed indicator is not working' (dialogue from the cockpit voice recorder). He then asked the co-pilot if his was working and received the reply, 'Yes, Sir.'

The interesting thing is they had 27 seconds to abort the take-off as there was more than enough runway to come to a safe stop. The airspeed indicator is a primary instrument—this should have rung alarm bells. In modern pitot-static systems, the system feeds the autopilot and some computers that monitor and control the aeroplane.

In the Air Accident Investigation program, "The Plane That Wouldn't Talk", Season 5, Episode 9. The narrator hinted that the decision to continue could have been a case of "get me home syndrome" or the infamous "press-on-itus" we discussed earlier as the crew had been away for some time.

As the flight progressed, the crew was met with numerous conflicting warnings of over-speed indications and under-speed indications, sometimes simultaneously. The pitot-static systems in modern jets have many feeds; a basic system has a pitot-static pressure for each pilot to measure pitot and static air pressure. The most probable cause of these conflicting warnings was a blockage in the captain's pitot tube, caused by an insect nest.

As it climbed, the airspeed indicator appeared not to be working. The co-pilot then said, 'It began to operate' which they interpreted as the captain's airspeed indicator beginning to function.

According to the investigation, the captain became very confused, made several decisions and then gave instructions to the co-pilot. Eventually, the stick shaker started to operate, a safety system that informs the pilot that the aircraft is about to enter a stall and actively do something immediately.

From the cockpit voice records, both the co-pilot and the relief captain made subtle hints to the captain on what he should do regarding flying the aircraft out of the stall regime. The captain is told what to do three times: "ADI" twice by the relief captain and "Nose down" by the co-pilot. The captain acknowledged neither until it became unrecoverable and the aircraft crashed into the sea.

What the captain asked for is max power on the engines, which made things worse. The aircraft had such a high nose-up attitude that one of the engines could not receive enough air to sustain sufficient airflow for the power required. Thus, the engine failed. The aircraft's wing lowered on the side of the failed engine, which caused the plane to enter a stall—this is where the aircraft's speed is not fast enough to allow the wings to produce a lift.

The aircraft quite literally fell out of the sky. Although this is salvageable and pilots train regularly for this event, they had lost so much height that it was unrecoverable by this time. The aircraft impacted the sea at such a high rate of vertical descent that the investigators discovered flattened coffee tins distorted so much by the forces they became discs.

Unfortunately, the investigation became difficult due to the aircraft wreckage laying some 700 feet below the sea. In months that followed, an investigation team from the Dominican Republic concluded the probable cause. 'The crew's failure to recognise the activation of the stick shaker as an imminent entrance to the stall and the failure of the crew to execute the procedures for recovery from the onset of loss of control.'

An aircraft accident, with all the error chain warning signs. If we list the events leading up to the accident, we can see the error chain-forming.

**Link 1.** The company was under financial difficulties and required costs savings to aid recovery. The company moved away from normal operations due to a costing review of procedures and processes. Often a reactive planning strategy will lead to sudden financial pressures, replacing a proactive planning financial strategy. Reactive solutions can lead to cutting corners to achieve company economic outcomes.

**Link 2.** Often assembling a team at short notice is another reactive planning strategy. The lack of roster planning for employee fatigue management coupled with an organisational culture of commercial pressure on the crew is terrible for morale and safety. Companies should accept the odd curved ball with a working environment that is safety conscious and utilises threat and error management (TEM) strategies.

**Link 3.** The team had a significant difference in experience—the captain had vastly more experience than the other pilots. Good TEM and team resource management would allocate an environment where crew members could assertively question a superior. A risk matrix with crewing data to identify possible crewing issues as higher risk is a good tool. I.e. crewing two inexperienced pilots on the same flight is a higher risk than one crew member with moderate experience and another less experienced.

**Link 4.** A breakdown of procedures—the pilot's primary flight instrument was not working and yet they continued the flight. We will never know why the captain elected to take off, yet it reflects my Shetland flight where we should have abandoned the sortie during the taxi phase. Task focusing is a common error in a breakdown of standard and emergency operating procedures, especially if one has been away from the regular operating base for long periods and is eager to return home.

**Link 5.** Mismanagement of a relatively minor problem is common when the person in charge elects to control the situation and becomes too involved. Rather than stepping back to manage the situation, the leader becomes task focused. Two crew members gave the captain the solution but were ignored; the bizarre thing is the people who see the solution then allow the one who doesn't know the issue to kill them eventually.

Like so many others, this accident had a subtle chain of events that ultimately led to a tragic and catastrophic loss of life. Note I used subtle as we are often so involved in our small role, we lose sight of the big picture that is conspiring to make us fail. Routinely in investigations, an audit of operations uncovers the potential risks sometime before the accident but the signs are either not seen or are ignored, often due to financial implications.

I could dissect this accident further; however, the points raised are valid and reflect the fundamental nature of this tragic flight. The chapter on threat and error management reveals a crucial component of all aspects of team resource management. You can be proactive against accidents by managing the threats through alerting people to said threats using good and active communication.

There is another serious side to accidents. Tragically, in this particular accident no one survived. Accidents affect people tremendously, whether you are directly involved or somehow related in one form or another. It is an incredibly stressful time for all of those affected, particularly if there are fatalities involved.

Over my aviation career, I have had the misfortune of being involved in some serious and not-so-serious incidents myself. I have lost more than 30 friends to aircraft accidents in my 38 years as an aviator. The vast majority of these accidents occurred while serving in the Fleet Air Arm in the UK.

The military has a different set of risk parametres compared to civilian industries. However, having been in the military at the start of its fledging crew resource management and watching it progress over the years, I am delighted to see the same principles being adopted as their civilian counterparts.

A serious incident or accident is without a doubt a critical event and it has a significant impact on individuals and companies alike. I have seen the good and the bad when handling accidents from a company's point of view. I recall a statement from my incident investigation course, 'There are always two sides to a story.' Opinions are often made with scantest of information, especially if there is notable previous history.

Commercial pressure is often brought to internal investigators as well. Accidents are incredibly costly to companies, even when they are not directly involved. The fatal EC225 helicopter accident in Norway on 29 April 2016 is a prime example. This accident grounded all EC225 helicopters globally, not just the operator of the accident aircraft. Suddenly, the revenue stream for all of the companies operating these aircraft was cut off with huge penalties involved.

Any hint of an accident due to bad practices will send investors into a state of panic and drop a company's share price. During company risk assessment meetings, one of the considerations is the impact on the business.

Companies are now under tremendous commercial pressure to find out what went wrong. Often a detrimental side effect to these investigations is it can quickly become a witch hunt. A company will always need visibility and portray they are actively doing something about the accident from a legislative point of view, from the governing body, from a commercial point of view or the investor's perspective. Putting companies in a difficult position; if they sack someone, staff will become reluctant to cooperate during investigations. If they do nothing about the cause, especially the human element, then the governing body and investors will penalise them.

To counter this, companies often introduce an ethical policy as part of their accident prevention strategy. The strategy encourages openness without retribution. In other words, be open with us and we will not punish you, even though transparency may reveal something wrong or bad practice.

Often referred to as a **just culture**, the just culture developed in the 1990s. It is a great tool that relies heavily on trust and participation by all parties. The area between a culpable or wilful act and a non-culpable act or a simple mistake is very grey. James Reason, Professor of psychology and co-founder of the Swiss cheese causation model, describes just culture as:

*An atmosphere of trust in which people are encouraged, even rewarded for providing essential safety-related information but in which they are also clear about where the line must be drawn between acceptable and unacceptable behaviour.*

Companies and organisations need to embrace that humans make mistakes and this is beyond their control. Rules and regulations help with our decision-making processes; however, they don't stop us from making mistakes or bad judgements. A just culture allows for openness and trust in the safety management system, striving to reach a common goal of safe and efficient operations.

Workers and staff don't want to have an accident or be hurt any more so than management. James Reason stated that,

'Organisations need to understand that people at the sharp end are not usually the instigators of accidents and incidents and are more likely to inherit bad situations that have been developing over a long period.'

Just culture strives to change conditions that breed unsafe situations in the workplace through honest and assertive reporting, which is retribution free. We need to understand it's purely built on a two-way trust between the management and staff. Once that trust is broken, it takes a long time to rebuild and in some cases, it can never be rebuilt entirely.

Quite often, critical information is lost in the white noise that surrounds these events. By white noise, I refer to an accident or incident where task-focused energy drives all people involved or sometimes those not directly involved.

Just culture is a system where the white noise can be reduced, allowing fast communication and openness. It begins at the start of an incident or accident regarding how people directly involved, witnesses and staff not directly involved are treated. Then becomes the benchmark on which just culture will be judged.

I was involved directly as a crew member on an aircraft in a serious incident, where a helicopter was severely damaged; fortunately, no one was injured. The conduct of the investigation and how we were treated as a crew was alarming to us all. I felt as if I were a criminal, although I was not even on the aircraft when the incident occurred.

Communication is the critical element of the start of an investigation. The opening statement of this incident investigation by the UK Air Accident Investigation Branch lead investigator says it all. He opened the interview with a very calm and reassuring tone and said, 'We are not here to apportion blame; we are here to simply get the facts and find out what actually happened.' His demeanour and the atmosphere in the room made me feel completely at ease. However, the company representative at this meeting was the complete opposite. He came across as pontifical and clearly out to protect the company position.

The company I worked for at the time could not be further from this if they tried. Their communication with me up to that point, apart from the local senior pilot, had been clipped and officious. The result of this behaviour was to make me defensive. I felt they had decided my crew and I was guilty and it was up to us to prove we were innocent.

It never fails to amaze me how some management personnel have lost the art of direct communication. There are ways to conduct an investigation and deal with an incident and there are legal procedures to help and protect all parties in any inquiry. They should not be used as a tool to intimidate witnesses and personnel who have involvement with the incident or accident. An excellent way to handle legal investigations and how they should be conducted is a neutral approach from the manager or safety officer. They should point out that it is for the mutual benefit of both the company and the individual.

A common legal requirement is to immediately conduct blood and alcohol testing after a serious incident or accident—a procedure that could be explained in an encouraging way to the individual concerned. For instance, 'This is to prove you were not under the influence of any drugs or alcohol, we must by law take certain measures to ensure these are accurate results, do you have any questions?' By saying it like so, you are promoting the just cause message.

You promote positive aspects to the procedure and still following legal processes.

The wrong way to address it is, 'You will be segregated and you are not to talk to anyone; you will then be taken to a medical facility and tested for blood and alcohol.' Essentially this was said to my colleagues and I, which made for a very stressful time after a potentially catastrophic accident where we luckily landed safely without harm. I can say the company at the time did not have a just policy. However, the implementation of just culture occurred not long after the accident and this company now promotes a "just culture policy" to this day.

I am a firm believer that people involved directly with an incident—i.e. the pilot in an aeroplane crash, the policeman in a high-speed chase or the surgeon in charge when a death occurs—should receive neutral help as soon as possible. Over time, support should be extended to more people involved, including those indirectly involved, such as close colleagues within a victim's department.

The opposite of a just culture is a **blame culture**; this can instantly alienate a workforce from the management team. What does a blame culture do during an incident or accident? It immediately hinders the investigation as the people involved simply clam up and thus getting non-biased information becomes near impossible.

I saw this first-hand in an internal company interim report of an aircraft accident. This interim report literally criticised the conduct of two cabin crew during the escape and survival phase of the accident. It was destroying the CRM culture built upon for many years, particularly the newspaper article that came out the day after the accident paralleled the report.

The cabin crew's actions had been conducted under extreme duress. Further to this and unbeknown to the author of the report, there was a design fault with the aircraft. This interim report caused broader implications for the two crew members involved, who suffered psychological difficulties post-accident and report.

David Marx JD in his paper, Patient Safety and the "Just Culture": A Primer for Health Care Executives' in April 2001 broke down unsafe behaviour into four behavioural elements described as the four evils.

**Figure 6b**
The four unsafe behaviours or four evils.

We can have simple **human error**, where a person has conducted themselves in such a way. As a result of that conduct, there has been an undesirable outcome because they failed to see the risk—for example, a simple mistake of miscalculating a patient's drug dosage.

**Negligent conduct** is a little more severe and the consequences make the individual more culpable. It has a precedent in common law that those found negligent shall pay relevant to the consequences if found responsible. I think it is easier to understand by definition: one should have known or been aware they were taking a substantial risk while taking care of something or someone. In the case of drug miscalculation, one has the use of a calculator that is just out of reach yet elects not to use it because they are in a hurry and accepts the risk.

As we progress through the behaviours, the culpability becomes more marked. **Reckless conduct** is different from the first two as a conscious decision is made to disregard a known and significant risk. For example, the nurse knows the drugs are strong anaesthesia and wilfully calculates the dose manually rather than using the calculator.

The final behaviour is easy for investigators—rules are rules; the consequences are specific in most cases. **Intentional rule violations** are when a person intentionally decides to violate a rule; all the investigator has to do is attempt to fathom out why the individual broke the rules. Often, the accused is aware of the risk and simply chooses to ignore it. In the drug dosage concept, the person is fully aware that company procedures state drug dosage must be calculated with a calculator.

One of the initial lessons I was taught in crew resource management was that as humans, we form our personality when we are children and this cannot be changed. Although modern thinking is that we can change our personality if subjected to extreme external traumas such as constant abuse or trauma. However, we can change our behaviour. Accident prevention and investigation is learning how to help people to change their behaviour.

Governing systems and companies also need to follow this guideline. Companies and organisations don't have personalities but they have corporate identities. They don't have to make behavioural changes but they can make company cultural changes. Companies and management teams cannot make an excuse, 'I knew nothing about this.' They can easily be found just as negligent, reckless and deemed to break the rules the same as any individual.

As discussed earlier, companies and management can often create an environment for an accident to occur. The staff do not merely inherit a bad situation, though individuals in a company may contribute to the error chain. The best thing a leadership team can do is create the right environment from the beginning so that the accident never occurs. Achieving this by working with their best asset—the people, their staff. By employing human-factors training, they can help their staff to see through the cloud of blue mist and identify the threats to prevent possible accidents.

# Chapter 7
# Stress

Stress is something that affects all of us, no matter your occupation. It presents like an emotion, although it has a very physical effect on your body. It is almost a taboo topic in the workplace, a challenging subject to discuss with anyone openly, friends or your family. It is subtle and can't always be physically seen; an excellent way to describe a stressed person is to picture the graceful swan with its webbed feet paddling like crazy underneath the water.

In certain groups or occupations, such as emergency services or the military, situations can be highly traumatic and very stressful. Stress and how we perceive it among the people who work in these occupations are often seen as weaknesses. In this cadre of professionals, who are often described as having the "rescue personality", stress is a natural and genuine phenomenon; however, it can be challenging to discuss openly.

The individual can perceive stress as a failure, 'This chap can't cope—he must be weak'. Everyone has their limit, a point at which it becomes all too much. The Oxford Dictionary of English defines stress as:

*A state of mental or emotional strain or tension resulting from adverse or demanding circumstances.*

Clinical definitions are far more subjective and modern descriptions first appeared in 1936 when Hans Selye defined stress as:

*The non-specific response of the body to any demand for change.*

He attempted to try and define stress satisfactorily throughout his life and struggled to explain his theories. He knew what he was trying to describe but just could not find a conclusive definition.

We have natural defences built into our DNA, often described as the "flee or fight" phenomenon. Our body prepares us when faced with a perceived threat by flooding our blood with chemicals, such as adrenaline. Allowing us to either run away quickly or provides us with the extra energy and strength to fight what is stressing us. However, if nothing comes of this, then there is an unnatural imbalance in our body chemistry. Called your homeostatic balance, we need the correct balance of many chemicals and gases in our body; this can be harmful if allowed to persist.

The homeostatic imbalance is what some believe leads to depression and anxiety. These symptoms are far more complicated, and many other factors may lead to these states of mental health.

As stress is such an individual state, the definition needs to be more subjective. The World Health Organisation has developed a much more individual description:

*The response people may have when presented with work demands and pressures that are not matched to their knowledge and abilities and which challenges their ability to cope.*

It is quantifying why some people seem to cope better than others when faced with identical situations. Professor Robert M Sapolsky describes these events as stressors, 'A stressor is anything in the outside world that knocks you out of homeostatic balance.'

There are many different stressors and some scientists have grouped them into specific stressor types.

- Environmental stressors (loud noises, overcrowding, leaky roofs)
- Daily stress events (baby crying, a lost umbrella, speed camera)
- Life-changing events (divorce, buying a house, bereavement)
- Workplace stressors (lack of job security, long hours, managerial demands)
- Chemical stressors (alcohol, tobacco, recreational drugs)
- Social stressors (demands of family or peer groups)

Einstein stated there is always an opposite, so there must be an opposing counter to stressors. Professor Sapolsky adds to his definition of stressors that a 'Stress response is what your body does to re-establish homeostasis. Trying to find a word to describe this is almost as difficult as finding a definition for stress. If you look at the opposite of someone who is stressed, we come out with someone who is relaxed. Thus, the opposite of stressor must be a "relaxer".' Below are counters to the above stressors:

- Environmental relaxers (soothing noises, open spaces, a dry and warm environment)
- Daily relaxing events (a walk at lunchtime, a pleasant cycle ride)
- Life-changing events (weddings, the birth of a child, paying off a mortgage)
- Workplace positives (job security, flexible working hours, pleasant working conditions)
- Chemical relaxers (alcohol in appropriate quantities, tobacco, prescribed drugs)
- Social relaxation (a couple of drinks at the local, or a coffee and cake with friends).

A fundamental problem with stress is that it affects individuals; differently, one person might actively seek what another finds stressful. Extreme sports are a classic example of this; some people find parachuting an absolutely horrific activity, while others seek out its thrill.

In regards to the workplace, some individuals thrive on responsibility and workload, whilst others find it incredibly stressful. The way to unwind for some is to go on holiday, whereas I find family holidays extremely stressful. Well, not the holiday itself but the travelling to the destination is stressful.

One of my friends has a very simplistic description of stress. If one were to imagine a jug—let's call it our "stress jug". The majority of us wake up happy or in a state of neutral euphoria. Only when we analyse the previous day do we start to either get more pleased, 'Wow, I had a great day yesterday' or sadder. 'What a total bitch of a day that was.' The jug is essentially empty when we are born and as we go through our daily life, we may be bombarded with positives and negatives, which constantly adjust the level of our jug, mimicking our stress level.

If you have had a succession of primarily bad days, then the level rises. As the jug level gets higher, our ability to shrug off bad things reduces. We become sensitive to friends teasing and jokes and, essentially, not as resistant to a minor annoyance. Reflecting our ability to cope—the more the jug fills, the less we manage. Eventually, we reach a point where we crack; even a little jibe or inconsequential event sends us over the top and the water in our stress jug cascades over the lip.

A similar thing occurs in stress tests in engineering, where a material or object is tested to destruction. A good example would be a support beam made from wood. The engineers would set up an experiment to define the exact weight that would cause the beam to snap and fail. Humans have a very definite point in which the weight of all the stressors placed on them will cause them to fail or snap.

The result of reaching that point seems to be proportional to the amount of stress placed upon the individual. Prolonged exposure to multiple stressors can lead to a complete mental and physical breakdown. Often found in the military, emergency services and healthcare professions subjected to various stressors in their daily working environment. This stress is cumulative and often over prolonged periods.

You can research on the Internet many written stress tests, which will indicate your level of stress. In 1967, two psychiatrists, Thomas Holmes and Richard Rahe, surveyed 5000 medical patients. They gave them a questionnaire and asked them if they had experienced any one of 43 life events in the previous two years. Each event was weighted with a score and then the total score calculated to produce a result that equated to the individual's chance of becoming ill through stress. Some scientists critiqued this test as different cultures react to events differently.

A common stressor in emergency and health professions is often hidden and very subtle. Often called perceived pressure, where one believes there to be a requirement to carry on and complete a task or risk some unquantifiable consequence. This stressor is perhaps the most dangerous one of all. The saddest is people believe they have some catastrophe hanging over them if they don't fulfil their goal or task. Often, the terrible outcome of this pressure is they take their own life, believing they have no other option.

When we examine the loss of this life, the investigators discover no real pressure existed or placed on the individual. It was perceived pressure leading to enormous stress and a total waste of a precious life. What is often the case, the person whose life was lost is generally a very valued member of society.

Commercial pressure, which is financially based, is a common pressure found in industry and the workplace. Effectively, it is management setting targets that have to be achieved by teams or individuals. In competitive industries, such as the resource sector, it is often a catalyst for stress.

One of my favourite movies is "The Forbidden Planet". In this classic Sci-Fi movie, a great quote aptly describes this perceived phenomenon "The monsters from the Id". Spoken by a dying scientist, who explains how the original inhabitants of a planet built a machine that can create anything they imagine. He refers to in the quote that the device has made a monstrous creature, which is sourced from the device's creators own subconscious minds. In the movie, the beast from the Id attacks and destroys the very thing that created it in the first place.

We all have our monsters from the Id. Perceptions of events can be metaphorically corrosive to the individual concerned, literally eating away at their mental well-being. The only way to combat this is to seek direct communication lines with the source of this pressure.

# Chapter 8
# Threat and Error Management

I first came across a formal approach to Threat and Error Management (T.E.M.) in 2008 after attending an instructor's course organised by the Australian regulatory aviation body, the Civil Aviation Safety Authority (CASA). It was very pilot orientated and emphasised that it was not a replacement for crew resource management training but rather complimented it.

I have a business partner who described the principle behind it; he said, 'It is a defensive flying course for pilots.' It is a defensive application to help you identify any threats or hazards to your operation and stop them from turning into accidents.

The origin of T.E.M was much the same as CRM; it began at the University of Texas in the United States of America. The university started a program called "Line Operations Safety Audit" or L.O.S.A. The original T.E.M and since then, many organisations have taken up this auditing process to explore the threats they faced.

The program places trained observers onto flights to observe flight crews performing routine operations. Particularly threats to safety during a flight, they also explored how they dealt with these threats. Finally, they examined if there were any consequences from the actions the crew took.

In L.O.S.A, they looked at threats and errors. So, what is the difference between a threat and an error?

A **threat** is an event outside the control of the flight crew. This threat must be managed to maintain safety margins or lead to an undesired aircraft state. A good example is a bad weather, such as turbulence. If the pilot does not reduce to the best speed for travel through turbulence, the aircraft may be damaged.

An **error** is an activity by the pilot that leads to a divergence from normal operations. If it is not managed or detected, then it can lead to an undesired aircraft state. An example would be an interruption to the landing checklist, after which the flight crew resumes the checklist. However, the landing gear item is then skipped, resulting in an unsafe aircraft state.

**Undesired aircraft states** are seen as the last stage before an incident or accident. Where the aircraft operation, configuration or position, is a direct hazard to the aircraft and safety of the occupants. In accidents and incidents, the mismanagement of threats and errors are often the main culprit.

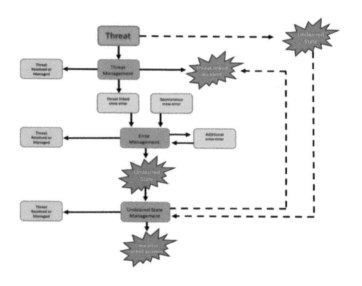

**Figure 5a**

Threat and Error Management Model (based on ICAO model)

More often than not, the crew are distracted and fail to see that the aircraft is becoming less safe. A friend of mine was killed in a naval helicopter accident in 1988; the helicopter had just taken off from a ship at night and crashed into the sea just minutes later. I saw the accident report about a year after in the Fleet Air Arm's safety magazine.

As I said at the beginning of this book, I won't criticise people's actions—there are always armchair experts after the fact. However, according to the report, it stated that both pilots got distracted by a flickering undercarriage light and failed to notice the aircraft's unintentional descent before it crashed into the sea. If we look at this accident in the context of T.E.M, it was an error.

Let's look at the T.E.M's model in another context, such as the medical industry. We know humans make mistakes, get distracted and have cognitive failures, so why would the medical industry be different? The team resource management course my business partners and I run showcases an excellent video. The video looks at an incident in a routine operation where a patient dies; the patient's husband is an airline pilot. He very articulately relates how there is synergy between the medical and airline industries and talks about safety programmes such as CRM and their effectiveness.

Before exploring case studies involving T.E.M, we need to look at the T.E.M model in much more depth. I have described the three main elements of the model: threats, errors and undesired states. In the latter, I have removed "aircraft" from the title to simplify to just an undesired state. A car accident could become an undesired traffic state or a medical accident during a procedure could become an undesired clinical state.

Threats and errors come in many guises and one of the findings of the L.O.S.A program was that not all threats and errors result in an incident or undesired aircraft state. If managed correctly, the threat or error is often avoided, often not realising that an accident or disaster was avoided.

Say we are driving down the road and it begins to rain but we fail to put the windscreen wipers on. It does not mean that we will automatically have an accident. Is it an undesired state? Below I have simplified the ICAO and CASA definitions stated in the Ian Banks, SafeSkies Presentation found on CASA's website.

*A condition that has arisen, which is undesired due to a lack of threat or error awareness and/or deviation from normal procedures, which reduces safety margins significantly.*

Road traffic rules govern how we drive our car; in most countries, they require you by law to have lights and wipers on in the rain. Hence, in the case above, yes, this would be an undesired traffic state. We have broken the rules and reduced the safety margin, increasing our chance of having an accident.

In most cases, we would turn on our wipers and reducing the chance of an accident. It does not eliminate the possibility of an accident as there always other threats that could lead to an accident. I think we apply T.E.M in our day-to-day lives; we just do so subconsciously. For the vast majority of us, we encounter numerous threats or errors and manage them well enough without it ever leading to an accident or incident, sometimes without even realising.

An error is no different outside of aviation. These errors can result from going outside the procedures laid down or from a lack of action to a scenario or event. A lack of guidance can cause mistakes; a good example is the operations staff on the Tartan oil rig during the Piper Alpha disaster. They continued to pump oil and gas into the Piper Alpha because they did not believe they had the authority to shut off the oil and gas from their management—even though they could see the rig on fire not 20 miles away.

In the middle ages, villagers would burn suspected witches but they did not understand that this was wrong; all they wanted was to remove a perceived threat to their livelihood and village. They believed they were doing a good thing, although their logic was naive at best. It seems a little brutal in the modern age but life was more challenging and people far more straightforward in the middle ages. Often, they would seek spiritual guidance from priests of the local village; if the priest said the woman was an evil sorcerous, then it must be true. Burning bodies to reduce the risk of disease was a common solution to hygiene and medical issues. Therefore, burning away the evil seemed an easy solution.

I have a very personal account to add now of an error made in the medical industry that ties into both a lack of situational awareness and threat management. The case is currently under investigation by the medical complaints body; therefore, no names or background information will be provided. It relates to a person known to me who had suffered a fractured leg due to a cycling accident. The fracture had essentially snapped the ball joint at the top of their thigh bone, which goes into his hip—requiring a surgical procedure to place screws through the bone and reattach the ball joint to the thigh bone.

On completion of the procedure and some rest, the patient travelled home from the hospital. During the next few months, the patient went through a rehabilitation program. The patient complained of almost constant pain in their hip joint while moving and raised this concern with their doctor. The doctor examined the patient and requested that they have an x-ray of the problem hip.

X-rays revealed a staggering conclusion that the surgeon had screwed too far into the bone. One of the screws protruded through the ball socket and into the joint itself. The screw head was effectively scraping against the inside of the joint wall on his hip. (Figure 5b is a reconstruction and not the actual x-ray of this person's hip). The person has since undergone another procedure to correct the problem and is still receiving treatment for pain and discomfort.

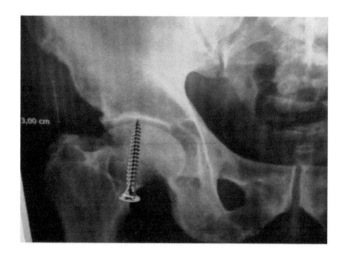

**Figure 5b.**
Reconstruction of the issue of the screw position

Let's look at the human factors and T.E.M issues in this case. First of all, what are the threats in this procedure:

- Infections.
- Use of the wrong drugs.
- Incorrect doses of drugs.
- Non-sterile instruments and dressings.
- Leaving surgical instruments and dressings inside the patient.

- Anaesthetic administration.
- Incorrect protocol or procedures.
- Wrong patient.
- The wrong area or limb on the patient.
- Power failure during operation.
- Equipment failure during operation.
- Communication difficulties due to surgical masks.
- Interruptions during procedures.
- Health issues with the surgical team, for example, fatigue.
- Preconditions with the patient

This list is not exhaustive and it covers the realistic threats that can occur. Save for the downright bizarre like an earthquake or an airliner crashing onto the building unless that is a real threat in your particular area, i.e. Christchurch in New Zealand, prone to frequent earthquakes.

We have established an error in this case study but where have the surgical team failed? They have been unable to recognise the risk, and hence, it has now become an undesired clinical state. The patient has not died or is not in any immediate danger of dying; the error has resulted in a situation that neither the surgical team nor the patient desires.

There are some minor errors or mistakes that may be inconsequential on their own; however, they lead to an accident when combined. These are called **error chains.** If you can break any of the links by removing a threat or error, it will prevent the accident from occurring.

In this example, we look at a classic scenario that anyone who has kids can easily relate with:

**Link 1.** A mother has to get the kids to school by car and the school has a strict policy on punctuality.

**Link 2.** One of her children won't get out of bed.

**Link 3.** She allocates time to getting the child out of bed, which makes her late preparing breakfast.

**Link 4.** One of the children has lost a school shoe, so she helps the child find it, making her later again.

**Link 5.** She gets the children in the car and starts it, only to find the fuel light has come on.

**Link 6.** She decides to risk it and get petrol on the way home.

**Link 7.** As she approaches a traffic light, it turns amber and she speeds up to make the light.

**Link 8.** Arriving at a road crossing, the car stalls due to fuel starvation and slows.

**Link 9.** Another car to the right, also in a hurry (link 8), jumps a red light on their side.

**Link 10.** The cars collide.

Often, error chains we describe as the "Swiss cheese accident causation model", which was developed by Dante Orlandella and James Reason of the University of Manchester. If you look at a block of Swiss cheese, it has random air holes through the block. If you slice the block, the holes appear in different positions on the slices. If you rearrange the slices in the right combination, a hole will appear in the same place through all the slices.

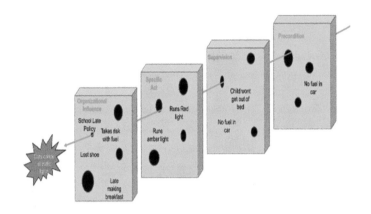

**Figure 5c**
The Swiss cheese causation model.

The model refers to the slices as defences against accidents happening. The holes are flaws in the defences and when all of these flaws align, the accident occurs.

Orlandella and Reason's model states that accidents can are traced to one or more of the following failure spheres: organisational influences, supervision, preconditions and specific acts. If we look at the scenario above, we can place the events or links into the spheres described in the scenario. Combining all the spheres put the mother's car and the other car involved at the exact place in time and space to have the accident.

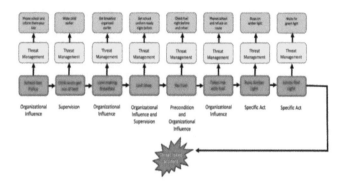

**Figure 5d**
Error Chain management

If we look at the chart in Figure 5d, we can see that the error chain could break by managing just a couple of threats. For example, if the mother had accepted, she would be upsetting the school's policy and called them to say she would be late, there would be no perceived pressure. Thus, the pressure would be relieved and she may not have been at the traffic light at the specific time of the accident.

However, it may take the removal of more than one threat to manage and avoid the accident. In this case, if the mother had checked the car had sufficient fuel the night prior and got school uniforms ready the night before, it could have changed the outcome significantly. Although, it does not mean she eliminates the threats.

Threats can change throughout the operation and new hazards can always appear, such as severe weather. The trick is to identify the threats and manage them before they combine with existing threats and cause another error chain.

We also have a psychological influence in threat analysis in decision-making; this is called mental bias. Another term often used is **cognitive bias**, a deviation from normality or rational judgement. When you are presented with a situation, you deal with it differently based on variables or influences, such as past experience.

The first of these is **expectation bias,** where we see what we expect to see, even if the reality is different. For instance, when I was growing up, I was a bit of a troublemaker. If something went wrong or got broken, my father would assume I was responsible. Most of the time, I was responsible; even if it was my brother, the expectation of people was, I was the culprit. My brother would often rely on this expectation bias to avoid punishment.

The missing S.A.R gear in the chapter on cognitive failure was an example of myself suffering from this mental bias. I saw the stretcher in its usual place and disregarded that it did not have the lifting straps fitted.

It is sometimes also known as experimenter's bias. The experimenter has a hypothesis of the outcome and concentrates on the evidence to support their expectation, disregarding or downplaying proof to the contrary.

Another mental bias that is commonplace is known as **specialty bias**. Speciality bias is when a person has knowledge in a specific field and prejudices their recommendations to their particular area of expertise—for example, a surgeon recommending surgery as a treatment instead of radiology or a course of drugs. Similarly, a nurse remarking during an operation and the surgeon saying, 'How could you possibly comment on this? You are not a surgeon.'

**Confirmation bias** needs to be correct, where a person seeks or interprets information that confirms a preconceived notion. I have seen examples of this in weak leaders or strong personalities who have a feeble argument. A leader imposes a new work practice in the former without seeking feedback from subject matter experts (S.M.E.) and then expecting success. When the shop floor provides negative feedback on their work practice, they seek information that will positively reinforce their original objective. Often heard from the leader involved is the phrase, *Just make it work.*

In everyday life, we come across situations where we must make decisions. A common cognitive bias in decision making is **framing error**. We focus on more positive outcomes to a problem and base our decision favourably towards positive reasoning. Another explanation is drawing different solutions to a situation with the same information, then establishing the answer on how that information is presented. Supermarkets and food producers are great at this: 'This yogurt is 90% fat-free,' says the labelling on a yogurt pot. Now, would you buy the same yogurt if the labelling said, 'This yogurt is 10% fat.'

One of my favourite mental bias is **fundamental attribution error (F.A.E.)**. To explain, let's return to the lady driving her kids to school. Say she is rushing to get to the school and cuts off another driver on the road. The other driver screams at the lady, 'Bloody woman drivers!' The other driver has placed their bias on personal beliefs rather than the situation or environmental factors. He cannot know that she is running late getting her kids to school or being distracted by them in the rear of her car.

When we place this bias on other people, we tend to concentrate on personal situations. However, when we discuss a mistake of our own, we tend to lean heavily on environmental or situational factors rather than personal factors. Once again, returning to our lady driver, she winds her window down and says, 'I am so sorry, the kids distracted me because we are running late for school.' She has used external factors rather than saying to the angry driver, 'I am so sorry—I am just an awful driver.'

If you conduct a little research into mental bias, it does not take you long to discover that we can have a very discriminatory way of looking at things. There are many more who would warrant mental bias being its own book altogether. One thing worth mentioning is that I have seen many times and, dare I say, have been susceptible to myself. **The focusing effect**, where you tend to place too much importance on one aspect of a task.

The focusing effect has a great nickname, "Press-on-itus". For instance, when we focus on getting home and don't see or choose to ignore, the threats that appear around us. Often in the Navy, after a long deployment away from home, we would be excited and longed to be reunited with our families and loved ones. All that remained was that last flight from the ship to our parent air station. However, sometimes the weather may be too marginal for that final flight home. We would focus on the things that would justify the flight rather than what went against the flight. On any other day, we would question the necessity of the flight and probably cancel. An alarming 69% of traffic accidents occur within 10 miles of a person's home.

| Distance from home | Percentage of accidents |
|---|---|
| <1 mile | 23% |
| 2–5 miles | 29% |
| 6–10 miles | 17% |
| 11–15 miles | 8% |
| 16–20 miles | 6% |
| >20 miles | 17% |

**Table 5a**

Table showing percentages of accidents relative to the distance from home. (Source: calculateme.com)

What are the solutions to preventing these errors and mental bias? With the growth of health and safety culture in everyday life and industry were risk assessing almost everything. What is now happening is we are managing our threats and errors in the form of risk assessments or threat analysis. Once we have gone through all the possible avenues of threat and errors, we then impose control measures to counter the threats and errors.

One of the best control measures is a checklist. We try to take the human part of the brain out of the equation by not letting it rely on memory; often, that is where we create mistakes. A word of caution though; checklists themselves can be a threat if not used correctly.

If we look at the surgical safety checklist in Figure 8e, it's an excellent tool for ensuring procedures follow a structured path. However, the threats discussed earlier still apply to its use. What if the surgeon elects not to use it and do it the old-fashioned memory way. What if there is an interruption to the person reading the checklist. Like all tools, the first thing to learn is how to use checklists correctly to be most effective. The organisational policy is an effective measure, where the rules state one must use the checklist.

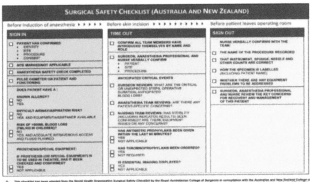

**Figure 8e**

The Australian and New Zealand surgical checklist

During the initial team establishment, at the opening brief given by the leader on the task, the leader should consider possible threats within the team and seek feedback. A good idea as sometimes we don't see all the threats and someone may have seen one the leader has missed.

Information at the scene of an accident is not always available to the team who have to deal with it. A typical situation for ambulance, police, fire crews, and S.A.R helicopter crews. What occurs instead is a dynamic risk assessment of the threats at the actual scene. A minimalistic approach to such complex tasks through instructions, checklists and standard operating procedures reduces the opportunity for human error.

I love the C.P.R acronym of D.R.S.A.B.C.D designed to be a simple tool to remember for the average person who performs a life-saving procedure. Yet in the heat of the situation, it might not always work.

**D.R.S.A.B.C.D:**
**D**anger
**R**esponse
**S**end for help
**A**irway
**B**reathing
Start **C.P.R**
Attach **D**efibrillator

I remember witnessing a traffic accident. I was around 30 seconds behind the nearest bystanders, some workers on their lunch break. They went straight to the car doors and started to extract the occupants. What they did not realise was the liquid pouring the engine while it was still going. I told them to move back, switch the engine off and then discover it was coolant and not fuel. If it had been fuel instead of coolant, it might have ended a little differently. The workers experienced tunnelled vision and missed the first D—D is for danger. Danger to the victim and threat to you. They had succumbed to blue mist and forgot the first sign.

In my career as a search and rescue aviator, we used similar acronyms to verbalise the risks on scene. It worked well and also helped the decision-making process. The L.I.F.E acronym tool I explore in the decision-making chapter is a good example. Organisational culture has to embrace threat and error management by incorporating it into procedures and risk management plans. The employees should be made aware of T.E.M and encouraged to be assertive and give feedback.

I wonder how many safety managers have do-it-yourself (D.I.Y.) accidents at home? Home accidents cause a significant loss to the workforce. ProChoice Work Gear's blog on D.I.Y accident rates states that hospital and emergency room admissions are up 54% and 22%, respectively; they also say that there are 2000 serious injuries in the state of Victoria alone. We must also learn to recognise threats in all situations. It applies at home as much as it does at work. Such as when you are operating a chainsaw on the overgrown tree in the driveway. Looking after the grandchildren by ensuring you have closed the pool entrance gate. By embracing T.E.M in our day-to-day life in addition to work, we will create a safer and happier life.

# Chapter 9
# Leadership and Management

Throughout our lives, we see many good leadership and management examples and then some atrocious ones. The question is, how can we achieve outstanding leadership and management when asked to undertake such roles? I hope to explore the attributes of a great leader or manager in this chapter and give you an insight into the particulars and pitfalls of this challenging subject.

Whilst I was preparing for my admiralty interview board to become a naval officer, I am asked often if leadership and management were the same things. The staff answer given to me at the time was no, they are not the same. In the modern era, as an officer you do not lead the unit; you command. The non-commissioned officers (NCO) do the leading. The officer manages the team for the greater good and broader picture you are privy to; the NCOs are not. This chapter will dissect both roles and find out how to be an exemplary manager and or leader.

# Leadership

*Leadership is a process of social influence, which maximises the efforts of others towards the achievement of a goal.*

Leadership, I believe, is simplistic and personal. The leader has to inspire and persuade those they are leading. In early historical military campaigns, the heads of tribes, nations or kingdoms tended to lead from the front. Still, the leadership role began to be delegated to generals as time passed. The word leader comes from the Anglo-Saxon word "lædan" meaning "to go forward as guide". In the fourteenth century, it began to trend more as a way to describe a leader.

In the twentieth century, the generals took a more managerial role. They directed the regimental leaders to supervise the battle, which in turn delegated the actual combat leadership role to junior officers and NCO's at a far more local level. Now, in the modern hi-tech era of warfare, this is still very much the case—although the days of battles across an open field are scarce since the war has become urbanised.

If we look at this in a civilian context, there has been a similar occurrence. Early industrialists, such as Henry Ford, founder of Ford Motor Company, had a more hands-on approach to his employees. Ford, seen often as too intrusive in the affairs of his workforce. He sent staff to inspect workers homes to see if they kept them clean and did not drink too much. As time went on, he reversed his views on the paternal aspect of workplace ethics and quoted as saying, *Paternalism has no place in industry* in 1922. He is often labelled as the founder of mass production; however, he was very shrewd in dealing with his workers. He introduced profit-sharing with his workers as an incentive to attract good-skilled workers and reduce the high turnover of his staff. He reduced the working hours and increased basic pay. His peers in other companies thought he was insane after placing a newspaper advertisement on a Friday stating the pay increases and reduced work hours. However, come Monday morning, 10,000 new workers turned up outside the Ford works, looking for employment at Ford.

I often look at companies with a high turnover of staff, which is a definitive marker for lousy leadership. In short, good leaders tend to attract good people to come and work for them.

In the modern era of industry, the welfare and control of the workforce are very much delegated at a local level. Chief Executive Officers (CEO) are merely figureheads to employees and in the larger companies they are very much distant. However, with the advent of technology, good CEOs will use social media and the internet to maintain contact with all levels of the workforce effectively.

Senior management teams direct and manages the workforce by utilising the supervisors' leadership skills and base managers on the ground level. Good companies nurture their ground-level leaders with programs intended to focus on these leadership skills.

One of the words often added to leadership is motivation. A great leader should motivate his or her team, which is where social influence comes in. The pillars of leadership refer to the principles of good human factors:

1. Communication
2. Moral courage
3. Integrity
4. Role modelling
5. Time management

## Communication

Communication underpins all and is a subject we looked at earlier in great detail. Around 65% of all disasters name communication as the leading cause. An example of poor communication is the ill-fated "Charge of the Light Brigade". During the Crimean war, a brigade of cavalry, some 600 men and horses, charged the masses of guns from the Russian Army.

Several factors contributed to the resulting disaster. The original order from the army commander, transcribed by an aid somewhat illegibly, and passed on to junior officer Captain Nolan. He then took the order to the commander of the Light Brigade, Lord Cardigan.

Despite its illegibility, the concept was that the messenger would answer any questions on the meaning of the general's order. Nolan was asked what guns, and he rather blasé replied, 'There are your guns, there!' The brigade was at the head of a large valley that split into two smaller ones. Unfortunately, they charged down the wrong valley and the rest recorded in infamy. The original order can be viewed at the National Army Museum in Chelsea, UK or by visiting the link in the footnote below.

*Lord Raglan wishes the cavalry to advance rapidly to the front, follow the enemy and try to prevent the enemy carrying away the guns. Troop of horse artillery may accompany. French cavalry is on your left. Immediate.*

On the flip side, you will find those outstanding achievements in history, such as the "Battle of Britain", excellent communication has been key to the successful outcomes. I am sure we can all think of some great public speakers who changed history by influencing a nation. One of my favourites orators is President John F Kennedy; my favourite quotes is: *Leadership and learning are indispensable to each other.*

Clear and concise communication is the best way to achieve leadership in any field; in the era of mass communication, it has become almost instantaneous. Therefore, it is even more important to relay your messages with care and great attention to detail. The slightest change to a text or email can read the complete opposite meaning of what you are trying to convey to the receiver.

Here's an example:

*Please can you mark all the equipment as per the directions in my previous email regarding helmets? Thank you.*

*Best regards,*
*Tony.*

In comparison to:

*Please* can you mark *all* the equipment as per the *directions* in *my previous email* regarding helmets! *Thank You!!*

*Tony.*

The former seems polite and straightforward; the latter written with some apparent venom. I once received a similar text on a Christmas day morning from a client; I will never know what this person was expecting. However, the way I dealt with it was by letting it go and replying after the holidays. If I had answered it immediately, I feel my emotions would have got the better of me, and the reply would have been in the same terse manner. Communication is a core subject and the central non-technical skill that we all need to learn to utilise effectively.

## Moral courage

A leader must have courage as an essential attribute; however, they must have moral courage too. You must do the right thing by your subordinates, particularly when faced with asking or informing them of something uncomfortable. During my working life in my military and civilian careers, I have had leaders who have simply avoided this or left it to others to perform. The very worst of these offenders just simply lied—the outcome of this is a devastating breakdown of respect for that leader.

There is also a fine line between destructive leadership and bullying. Bullies are always cowards. When a leadership role empowers you, it is easy to use your status to avoid challenging issues or situations. Bad leaders will often end the conversation abruptly and expect you to cease reasoning to avoid further confrontation or to have to explain themselves.

Another example of a lack of moral courage is hiding behind status or blaming your superiors for the misfortune you must convey to the employees.

If a leader has moral courage, they will gain the respect and trust of their subordinates and their managers. To achieve this, you must stand by them, be honest and have the courage to tell them like it is. As a leader, you will build trust and understanding so that when things get tough, your team will hold you in good stead and be behind you when you need them to be. A South American company was handed over from the owner to his son, the son spent time getting to know the workers and seeking out the issues that vexed them. He discovered that the workers hated the managers; they did not trust them and felt they were ineffective. What the son did was sack the majority of the managerial workforce after reviewing their performances. He then set up a workers committee to work with the remaining effective managers collaboratively. The result was transformational; the company become very successful. An interesting by-product was that during the lean times and staff cuts had to be made, the staff themselves worked with the managers. The staff themselves sorted out redundancy and early retirement positions with little input from the management.

# Integrity

Integrity goes hand-in-hand with moral courage. You are doing what is right as opposed to what may be the easier path. I have always believed in fairness—if you favour someone more than the others, you will fracture the team.

It can be difficult as you may have a member of your team who is a quick and accurate worker. It is always easy to use them to get the work done if you need to have a quick job done rather than contact another team member who is slower but just as accurate. The problem with this is that your faster person may feel they are doing all the work and the other team members are getting away with less work.

Often within a team, there is a perceived feeling of unfairness. Although, this may be a mistaken view that other members are getting better treatment. I saw this at a search and rescue base where I once worked. The unit had become split between local staff and staff who flew in on a fortnightly touring cycle; the local staff felt that these touring staff did less work than them. I was not in any leadership role; however, I enjoyed the work and my friends, which I had on both sides of the coin, local and touring (I was a local).

I went through the last year's rosters and made a spreadsheet of how many shifts each person had performed and how many weekends everyone had worked. Surprisingly, the results showed that the touring staff did more shifts than the locals and in fact they worked the most weekends. Showing everyone the actual facts and stopped any animosity from occurring.

In dealing with your team on an equal basis and level playing field, you create a harmonious and happy workplace. Remember, there are very few bad workers in the workplace or if there are, it is probably not that the employees are bad but instead they are poorly led.

## Role modelling

Professionalism and good work ethics are essential in a leader. If the leader skips work early every day, then they will rapidly lose all aspects of respect from their team. Correspondingly, is the team expected to finish the daily tasks if the boss is seen slacking off? Appearance is essential as well as following the company rules. A boss who clearly defies all aspects of the company ethos and regulations will lose the team's admiration.

If you disagree with company policy, such as dress code, you cannot be seen to clearly disobey the company rules by not wearing the appropriate clothing required. A more assertive action would be to come up with an alternative answer, pass it up the chain using the correct grievances procedure and show you as a role model for those who may feel the same way.

## Time management

A leader must have excellent time management skills. Being punctual with tasks given to you by management or your team promotes your professionalism as a leader. If you get given a leave request and then sit on it for weeks, this will result in total disrespect from your team members—management too if they find out about it.

Learning to allocate time to achieve tasks is an excellent way to build trust from people above and below you. If you feel you have too much on when the boss gives you yet another task to do, ask them which of the other functions they would like you to drop or delay.

The best description of good leadership I have heard of is one from my father, 'Leadership is like a piece of string.' What Dad was saying was, 'If you push a piece of string, it goes all over the place. However, if you pull a piece of string, it will always go straight and true.'

I have since improved upon this. Often a string is made up of strands like a shoelace; for instance, by putting a knot at each end of the string, it will stay together and pull true. Applying this to a leadership context, by briefing your team at the beginning and de-briefing them at the end, they will follow you and find it easier to conduct the task.

Leadership comes easily to some but to others, they will have to work at it. One of the funniest observations I have heard about a person's leadership skill was from an officer's army report I saw while on a staff course. The only reason your soldiers follow you is out of curiosity.

An amusing but telling statement, which says it all, 'You can learn leadership but for some individuals, it will take time and a few mistakes along the way.' I have certainly made some terrible leadership decisions but I have learned from them and ensure I never repeat the same error.


## Management

*To manage is to forecast and to plan, to* organise, *to command, to coordinate and to control.*

Managing is just as important as leading; it is doing the same job but with the bigger picture as an influence. While similar to leadership, it aims to improve the company or unit as a whole rather than at an individual level. In management, delegation is the key element as you simply cannot cover all bases. The bigger and more complex business or operation, the more delegation required. If we look at the origins of the word management, it comes from the Italian word "maneggiare", meaning to handle, as in a team of horses or tools. The Italian word has its origins from two Latin words, "manus" meaning hand and "agree" meaning to act.

The most common statement I hear when managing goes wrong is bosses who are accused of "micro-management". Undermining the leaders trying to achieve the task, the managers set them and make the employees wonder if their leaders are capable or empowered enough to accomplish the task.

Over-control of people is known as a dictatorship. In my career, I have even heard managers or empowered personnel actually state, 'Well, this is a dictatorship, not a democracy. Some may argue that on some occasions, a dictatorship is more appropriate. I agree to some degree; if you look at the downfall in some countries of the dictatorships, the aftermath is often anarchy.'

Tito in former Yugoslavia is an excellent example of this. Once he died, the Balkans became a powder keg. There were century-old disputes and bitterness combined with vast amounts of stockpiled weapons provided due to a strategy of the old Soviet bloc. The Soviets believed they would be overrun and hid vast stockpiles of arms to initiate guerrilla warfare within the invading forces captured territory. In summary, you had a dictatorship regime removed and a vast number of stockpiled arms in an area with age-old disputes—the perfect setting for a civil war.

The military has some great examples of managers throughout history, take Lord Nelson, for instance. He had an overall plan to win the battle and delegated the execution of his plan to individual captains who he trusted to use their own judgement and achieve what he desired.

Captains of industry are much the same, they have an overall plan that needs to be instigated and they delegate down to managers to bring about their wishes. Steve Denning, a writer on radical management, has written some great articles on management change. He refers to managers being instigators for small organisational teams to achieve the work. These small teams report to the client, not the manager. The concept behind this is that the client gets what they want, not what the manager thinks the client wants.

I have seen managers many times at client meetings simply not listen to the client's requests and insist on delivering their version of the client's needs. I found it very frustrating and I can only imagine how frustrating the client found it. The best companies these days on competitive markets give the client or customers what they want.

Steve Jobs, the late boss of Apple, said it well, 'Great things in business are never done by one person; they're done by a team of people.' He was known for a somewhat abrasive management style; however, he brought everyone together in the one common goal. His brilliance was getting all the teams in Apple and us, the clients/customers, to believe in his vision.

Steve Job's quote can apply to all, even some surprisingly individual achievements. Andy Murray, the British tennis player, thanked his team upon winning the Wimbledon Men's singles final for the second time. Even though it was his individual effort on the court, his team supported him to achieve that common goal in numerous ways. Hence, it was not so much Andy's goal but the goal of the whole team.

The best leaders and managers can build their organisational team, delegate different roles to smaller groups within the organisation and bring everyone together to achieve a common goal. In my own company's organisational chart, we have not adopted the traditional hierarchal pyramid style of company leadership structure charts.

Each time lines cross is a line of communication.
Therefore ANY team member can communicate with ANY OTHER Team Member to further the goals of the company.
Whether a large or small team it is perfectly acceptable to talk to anyone in the company.

Chart 10a. Airmid's organisational chart

Instead, we have a circular chart (Chart 10a); the idea is to create open communication channels between everyone. Whilst this is an excellent way of opening up means, of employees and managers to communicate. It must be understood that the company's boss holds the responsibility and leadership role and has the final decision on company policy, of course, based on advice from his or her team leaders.

# Chapter 10
# Teamwork

*The combined action of a group, especially when effective and efficient.*

British Oxford Dictionary of English (Apple OS 10.11.5)

When I think of team work, I picture the New Zealand "All Black" Rugby Union team. They seem to know if they pass the ball back, one of their team will be there to catch it. I feel that it is almost magical to watch or poetry in motion as some would say. So, what is it that makes the All Blacks such a wonderful team?

In 2004 the All-Blacks coach, Graham Henry, held a meeting with the All-Blacks leadership team over three days. In this meeting, they formed a way forward; they looked at the human aspect of rugby and came up with a plan and a new phrase: *Better people make better All Blacks*. They worked on their team both on and off the rugby ground. James Kerr, the author of "Legacy", a business book that uses All Blacks as inspiration, wrote an article on this strategy in 2013.

Kerr described how the team blueprint worked around six pillars:

1. Devolved leadership—empower the players with purpose or intention and trust them to deliver.
2. Individual learning development—chart individuals progress throughout their time with the team.
3. Create a learning environment with a philosophy of continual improvement—Henry used the phrase "Champions do extra" to emphasise the point.
4. Train to win—ensure training is more challenging than the match on Saturday afternoon. As the military says, 'Train hard, fight easy.'
5. Identify sources of stress and how they affect human performance.
6. Form a bonding ritual—in this case they reinvented the famous haka and called it Kapo o Pango.

After this change in team development, they proved their success on the rugby field. Their win ratio went from 75–82%, becoming the most successful rugby team in the world with 20% more wins than the nearest rival.

I think most people will have experienced being in a dysfunctional team at some point. It is frustrating, upsetting and lowers morale. If the team does well, individuals feel excellent and confidence increases. However, when it goes wrong, many things can happen. Including:

- Morale drops
- Productivity drops
- Accidents increase
- Fragmentation of the team—cliques form
- Absenteeism increases
- Discipline declines

It becomes a self-perpetuating downward spiral, so how can we change and develop an effective team? Utilise a simple solution and obtaining an effective leadership strategy. There are many blogs and online learning sources that cover this subject. Most focus on the principle of team development and setting common goals, working together on achieving these goals and recognising successes.

During an exit interview with my ex-business unit director, I was asked how the company could improve. My answer focused on two points: 'A company's best assets are its people, not its machines,' and 'Leaders need to be proactive, not reactive.' When you have to be reactive, I added, 'Don't use a sledgehammer on the problem, use the appropriate tool to solve the issue.' If you fire someone who has made a mistake, you take away an opportunity. As long as the person was not deliberately violating the regulations or policy and it was a genuine error. Keep them as an asset; that person will not make the same mistake and will also educate other workers about the errors of their ways.

I have developed many teams over the years and the first step is straight forward—find out the individual's strengths and weaknesses. This may take a while, so it's essential to maintain focus on the common goal and ensure the entire team is aware of this goal.

In sport, it is evident; the goal is to win the game. Statistically speaking, you are bound to lose a game at some point. In teamwork mentoring, the trick is to believe you have made a difference, even if you lose the game in the end.

I watched an All-Blacks game where they were losing right up until the final siren. Interestingly, they did not change their demeanour; in fact, they managed to obtain and keep the ball, scoring a swift try in extra time. Their unwavering belief that they could do it and that kept the team together and proved them successful.

When you have identified each individual's strengths, next use them to achieve a common goal. Often the team that comes together behind a common goal will be successful and work efficiently together. I have seen this in a team-building exercise where a successful teams smiles and congratulations to each other upon victory say it all. Hollywood blockbusters are great for showcasing this with lots of whopping and hollering and excessive backslapping. Movies such as Star Wars, Independence Day and Top Gun, to name but a few, have great examples of this at the conclusion of their films.

Now, to explore what good teamwork looks like, let us return to commercial kitchens. How do they all manage to achieve their individual roles effectively and deliver a great meal together? I can hazard a guess that we have all come across some bad or good examples of meals from restaurant kitchens. Formula One motor racing shows excellent teamwork in the incredible skill and timing of pit stop crews. It's genuinely unique how they manage to get the cars fuelled, tyres changed and have them back in the race quickly.

My final example of a great team is emergency room staff, mainly when dealing with mass casualties. The quiet, professional manner they use while saving lives through assessing and triaging is astounding. What makes the above occupations so good at teamwork? Well, it is all down to a few fundamentals:

1. Someone has to be in charge—an effective leader who can quickly gain the team's trust.
2. The said leader must brief the team and lay down team goals and the guidelines that will achieve them.
3. The leader must lead by example—they must encourage and support where it's required.
4. The leader and team must demonstrate situational awareness. The team has to keep the leader informed and the leader must have an overall understanding of how the task is progressing.
5. Finally, the leader must provide feedback during and at the completion of the task.

Why are guidelines important? People in complex tasks or scenarios with multiple functions to complete need to have some support. They need to have structure to achieve a successful outcome, mainly when something goes wrong. We need to take the human element out of the equation and a guideline is an effective way of doing this.

In aviation, we use checklists to achieve complex tasks. Aviators go through standard lists to start engines and prepare aircraft for flight but most importantly, they have checklists for emergencies. Giving the flight crew a set of procedures to resolve the problem and hopefully achieve a safe outcome.

The book "The Checklist Manifesto" by prominent surgeon Atul Gowanda looked at lessons from the aviation industry and how it could benefit the medical sector. Gowanda attended a meeting discussing operating theatre procedures, including clinicians and medical industry personnel at the World Health Organisation (WHO) headquarters in Geneva. While speaking, he asked the question, 'Are there any global guidelines for global public health programs?' This question was met with some cynicism and disbelief that he would ask such a question.

He thought of how he could spread the importance of procedures and guidelines to reduce deaths in surgery on a global scale. It had to be a simple theory; thus, he suggested an international checklist for surgical procedures and met with a more positive response from the meeting participants.

He explored the checklist concept and stripped it right back to basics; then, they experimented with a surgery checklist with his team. He encountered several issues along the way and the biggest was how to use a checklist correctly. Checklists could refer to a simple check-off or "tick" list but what happens if you're interrupted during the checklist? He discovered checklists are not the golden answer to team effectiveness rather a tool. A team needs to all be on board with the concept and understand how to operate with a checklist to work effectively.

Gowanda discusses one of the most significant destructive and toxic forces in a team. He labelled it "Silent disengagement". I must admit that I have seen it many times in different guises. Referring to those individuals who refuse to work as a team because 'It's not my job.'

Teams must have redundancy. There was a time when I needed to take personal leave and I remember my boss at the time saying, 'No one in the Royal Navy is indispensable.' He was right. If you step away from work or go on holiday, does the whole workplace grind to a halt? It might slow down but the leadership team need to keep the company going, so they will find a way around any absence in the workplace.

Good teams and leaders improvise—they learn each other's duties or ways to bypass the productivity gap. In the military, they practice reducing the team by constantly simulating casualties in exercises. It is something that aviation also does when we practise pilot incapacitation. When I initially started in civilian search and rescue, we only talked about the procedures for pilot incapacitation. I then introduced technical crew incapacitation as the person more likely to be debilitated was the rescue crewman—the flesh and bone on the end of the winch wire.

Another big issue in teams who face emergencies is when a person's perceived lack of authority prohibits them from acting—as in the Claymore rig continuing to pump oil to the Piper Alpha.

Occasionally, there are toxic influences in a team. By this, I mean some individuals have limited human-factor non-technical skills. For example, a person who talks badly about a team member to another behind the victim's back. I have worked with these people over the years and I have seen how they can destroy the team from within; sometimes, it only takes one individual to bring a whole team down.

These individuals often manipulate other team members to get their own way. I once heard of an individual who would instigate shift swaps with other colleagues to get a particular day off from a roistered shift. He would ask one person to swap with him, then once that was agreed, get another person to change with that person until he ended up with his preferred day off. These roster swops would repeatedly happen, which undermines the person in charge of rosters, not to mention upsetting his colleagues. Eventually, other toxic behaviours caused management to move him to another base.

At its worst, this behaviour can result in people going above the hierarchal management system in place. Individuals who go over the head of a manager and straight to the boss with issues. They are extraordinarily unprofessional and need to be dealt with by their elected manager. The manager must reemphasise the chain of leadership and inform them that what they have done is inappropriate and not the proper procedure for addressing their issues.

Often these individuals will form cliques in the work environment and berate other employees behind their backs. I had heard of and once fallen foul over this sort of behaviour, mainly when I worked in a company with a system of bases around the country. Rumours and gossip would become part of the daily life on a SAR base, especially when the crews spent a lot of time doing not much between rescues.

I had some issues in my training, which was not solely my fault because of a very irregular training period. I recall settling into a new unit and I started tuition in my new permanent base, where I had a couple of great trainers who worked with me and helped me pass my training. Sometime later, there was a minor incident when I was the on-duty winch operator and my winchman (and chief crewman) fell over on the deck of a Russian fishing boat while he was unattached to the winch wire, and the aircraft was a distance away.

The aircraft was about 500m away, awaiting a call from the winchman to pick him up. We recovered him and he informed us that he had hurt his back when he fell. The incident was discussed at the debriefing, and I thought nothing of it. About a month later, I was informed by the chief crewman that I was to be given a check by the company standards crewman as there was some doubt about my competency as a SAR winch operator.

The chief crewman was quite angry about this, as was the base manager, while I was absolutely heartbroken. I felt betrayed and furious when I called an old friend from another unit. He told me there was a rumour that I had bashed the winchman all around the Russian vessel and seriously hurt him. Three individuals had then spoken on the phone between bases about it and hence it got the attention of the standards crewman. Not one of them asked the chief crewman or me what had happened.

At this point, I wanted to resign as the mere thought that someone on the base had deliberately tried to get me sacked was unacceptable to me. I spoke to the standards crewman on my return to the base and he talked me out of it. The head of standards was on the same unit as me and I spoke to him about it. He was quite perplexed as there was a procedure for this sort of thing and it had not been followed. I agreed in the end to have a regular annual standard check a few months later and passed it with no issues. Thus, as far as standards and myself were concerned, the matter was closed.

The handling of unusual human resource issues in teams is essential, poorly conducted and can quickly ruin a good team. I have seen this on many occasions where bad leadership and decision making split great teams apart and it takes excellent leadership and arduously hard work to reunite them.

These troublesome individuals require tight handling by utilising good leadership skills, they need to be reined in and shown the errors and consequences of their actions. If your team has had human-factors training and frequently practice

133

their non-technical skills, then there is no room for these individuals to move and they will either fall into place or leave.

# Chapter 11
# Culture

*The ideas, customs and social behaviour of a particular people or society.*

British Oxford Dictionary of English (Apple OS 10.11.5)

What is culture? We have looked at just culture in a previous chapter but now we are referring to a much broader scope of the word—a combination of just culture, safety culture and positive culture. While I have mentioned the first two before, what does positive culture incur?

**A positive culture** is a culture where individuals are positive and assertive; they politely give opinions without anger or venom. It is a culture that values opinions and strives for the greater good of the community, be it socially or at work. Based on a two-way street, people accept other's views and it is taken in return or at least met with peaceful dialogue, retaliation free.

**Organisational culture** plays a significant role in the workplace and an organisation creates its own culture through their day-to-day practices. This culture can range from leadership training to the handling of crises. Unfortunately, large corporate giants tend to have a difficult job when it comes to promoting a healthy positive culture due to their size and often the geographical scope.

The other problem with large organisations is the levels of leadership; the chances of the lowest sector being able to talk to the highest level of the organisation is remote. A company worker may see a CEO once in a few years and even then it will only be for ten minutes. However, modern-day communication mediums make it easier for organisational leadership to pass their message to the general populace almost daily, which is good, although distant and sometimes impersonal.

Organisations create culture but it is individuals who can cause havoc with the atmosphere of a workplace. I once worked on a unit where a co-worker had been convicted of a serious and socially inappropriate crime. The person who committed the offence maintained it was a mistake and while half the people believed him, the other half did not. It created the most toxic atmosphere I have yet to come across again. Even though outwardly professionalism remained, in the background, there was some awful back-stabbing and general nastiness.

A similar case I came across during an interview with a prospective Winch Operator when I was the chairman of the company interview panel. We asked the candidate a standard question 'Have you ever had to deal with a difficult person or situation?'

His honesty surprised me and I instantly recognised a young man who had excellent communication and human factors skills. His present employer was a helicopter provider in the EMS market and had rescue crewman who was subcontracted, paramedics. Before he started with them, they had suffered a fatal accident and a paramedic had been killed during a rescue.

He explained how an atmosphere of mistrust developed after the accident and a division between the helicopter company and the paramedic's company was widening. He told us how through patience and good communication, he bridged the division and regained the confidence of the paramedics in the helicopter provider.

Employees will soon find out what a workplace is like— the "good" guys and girls and the "bad" boys and girls. I have been fortunate to work in some great work environments where the organisational culture was open, friendly, professional and everyone worked together assertively. One example was a multi-cultural and ethnically diverse workplace where my co-workers embraced each other's culture and used it to improve the overall atmosphere.

An open and just culture allows for open debate and assertiveness to flourish. For instance, if a worker sees what isn't working on the shop floor, they have an avenue to express these findings to a receptive and open-minded management structure.

How do we encourage such openness? Confidential helplines are one method, particularly with societies with a "face saving" culture. Equally, these programmes can have a detrimental effect on societies with a different culture. Australians know it as "dobbing in your mate" and frown upon these tattletales, as they prefer an upfront and straight to the point approach.

A problem with these programmes in the workplace is the fact we are human. It is in our nature to be judgmental and there is no one more judgemental of you as a leader than a subordinate. Your average worker will make their mind up about a management system, safety reporting or management tool designed to improve workplace culture. They are not only a company's greatest asset but also one of the greatest critics.

Communication here is critical once again; open dialogue within the workforce will get them on your side. You don't have to tell the workforce commercially sensitive information; merely justify your actions in an assertive manner. Honesty is also paramount; management and supervisors will quickly lose all confidence placed in them by the workforce if given untruthful information by their superiors. The company defines the culture by management structures, policy implementation, and by commitment to these policies.

I met a CEO a few years ago who had a great relationship with their average worker. He introduced a Code of Business Integrity (COBI) implemented quickly and administered by human resources. Yet because the average worker may not be subjected to bribes or corporate hand-outs, they felt no need to sign up for this policy. As a result, disciplinary action was then threatened and it became a rather heated and very debated topic.

When one of the senior managers from headquarters visited the workforce, he had to deal with some rather hostile employees (I know, as I was one of them) who very assertively expressed their views on COBI. The worker's argument made sense to the manager, and instantly he saw the problem. What was missing was the bigger picture, which needed to be explained. Managers don't always have to let the employees know every corporate issue broader consequence. However, on this occasion, it needed to be and was not explained at all. The company had a legal obligation to ensure all workers were subject to COBI and they needed to show 100% of the workforce were compliant with this code. The company was at risk of a considerable fine if they did not prove they had 100% compliance. This senior manager explained it eloquently, although he did not give away all the information from a senior corporate level, just enough so the workers understood why they must comply.

Knowledge is power; it is a phrase I have often heard from co-workers. What this refers to is when a manager or supervisor keeps all information to themselves. It will work some of the time, but they must divulge a little to allow the team to complete a task sooner or later. If the team don't know what the end goal is, how can they possibly finish the task?

We, as humans, build preconceived notions of culture—both the culture at work and outside of work. A good work acquaintance told me one night at a bar, 'There are no tribes in our company.' It was an ironic statement; when I looked at our co-workers in the bar, they all sat in distinct groups, dependent on the type of helicopter they flew or were engineers, or if they were admin staff.

I attempted a little social experiment to get those from different helicopter backgrounds to talk to each other. I asked one guy to discuss his opinion on a subject with another worker from another helicopter type. They temporarily moved to the other group, but they returned to their specific social circle as soon as the conversation stopped.

I don't think aviation companies are different to the rest of society. If you conducted the same experiment in a chocolate factory, I believe the same would happen. Social groups form in various departments in every workplace and generally, workers stick to their own group. Creating a culture that allows for open and transparent communication can overcome social divides and get the whole company or team working towards the common goal.

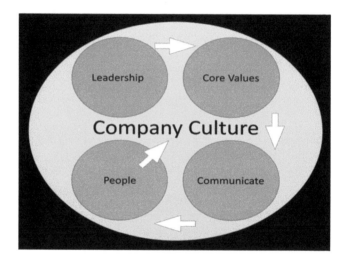

**Figure 13a.**
Organisational tool for changing minds

How do we change a culture in the workplace that is bad, toxic, and has mistrust? The best way to implement a cultural change is to look at their core values and mission statement. Allow the leadership team to align their processes with their core values, and the message will spread from there. By using the core values to inspire change, you are not forcing a change upon the organisation. Use the company's resources to build the shift through good communication with workers in the company.

Unfortunately, organisational change can only come from the top. Only after an organisation's leaders recognise a need for change can they then implement it. Often, only after an accident occurs when this change is forced upon an organisation, which is tragic and too late.

Organisational culture is elementary to spot. I remember visiting a small charter airline in the Pacific Islands and seeing the pilot board in their operations room (see Figure 13b). Although organisational culture can be pretty subtle, what do you glean from the culture at this airline by looking at this information?

**Figure 13b**
Factious pilot currency board.
(Names and dates bear no relevance to any charter airline or
personnel for demonstration purposes only).

I assumed that the chief pilot and his deputy do not lead by example as some of their checks are expired. Often this is a sign of the leadership motto: 'Don't do as I do, do as I say.' I have come across many bosses, although in their defence, they are sometimes too busy to stay in check with company requirements.

The last column for CRM struck me as a little frightening yet amusing in a way. Many assumptions come to my mind; I imagine an old-fashioned chief pilot who saw CRM as irrelevant and not applicable. Perhaps it was in the airline's culture to allow supervisory managers to run operations how they saw fit and to disregard their checks blatantly, or perhaps to overwork them, so they had no time to conduct their checks. It could also be the national regulatory body's culture, where CRM training is not mandatory.

CRM in developing nations is ongoing, although it often hampered by lack of funding, aging aircraft and an emphasis on the pilots themselves. It also parallels with medical industries in the developing world, which suffer from the same issues of funding, resources and stress on the medical staff.

Team resource management should be driven from the top and filtered down to the industries that require it. It does come down to funding a lot of the time—why spend money on training, which legislation does not need to be incorporated? Even in countries with legal requirements, how the industry adopts the principle is only regulated by those enforcing the standards.

While some organisations put the appropriate funding in, others do the bare minimum. In some cases, CRM training consists only of the candidates watching a video. It is only after an accident or incident that the regulators step in to create proper CRM/TRM culture by introducing the legislation at a government level or the government's regulators implement a higher level of enforcement in CRM

/TRM training. There is now a growing acknowledgement of human factors. I feel we are not far from having regulatory processes in place to spread team resource management into other industries and emergency service providers.

It is all about the culture of the regulators, companies and organisations they regulate. We are all too often these days in a tick the box culture as opposed to sorting out the real problem – it is the humans that make the mistakes. Good company culture recognises this and adopts the training to address the human issue, not just tick the boxes with a safety management system and a workplace safety audit.

# Chapter 12
# A Case Study

## Flight CHI 9: S-92A C-GZCH accident

In the following four chapters, I am going to look at case studies from different industries. The purpose of this is to show you, the reader, that human factors are the catalyst in most accidents, no matter what industry you work. The first two are from aviation and show two very different types of accidents.

I would like to study first a specific aircraft accident and dissect the official report to investigate the human-factors elements of an actual accident. Material from the official report is reproduced with permission of the Transportation Safety Board of Canada. My aim simply is to look at the human factors in this accident. I hope that having read the previous chapters, readers will also see the relevance of human factors in this tragic accident.

Flight CHI 9 was a helicopter charter flight ordered to take 16 passengers out to an oil rig off the Canadian coast. Some 54 nautical miles off the coast, the aircraft suffered a malfunction and began to lose gearbox oil. The two-flight crew attempted to diagnose the malfunction and turned towards the land; the helicopter crashed into the sea with one survivor out of the 21 total persons on-board.

At the time of the Flight CHI 9 accident, I was involved in SAR training with a significant offshore helicopter provider in the resource sector and thus was given access to the report. The regulatory body was definitively aware of the report as the document was given to my source by the regulatory body. The search and rescue, safety equipment and CRM issues are clearly stated in the report. Yet, reluctance to implement the recommendations is plentiful in similar areas of operation.

Issues found by the report are identical in many instances to those I tried to resolve in my region at the time. Sadly, the Canadian information had little to no effect and the limited search and rescue (LIMSAR) style of operation is still the standard model at the time of writing this book. In fact, due to the oil price crisis, some operations have even scaled back their SAR capability.

The issue is in areas outside of government-provided SAR assets; company self-help is the only option for the resource industry. At the end of the day, SAR is like insurance; you have to pay for it and hope you never have to use it. Safety always comes with a price, and the history in Australia is pretty good as the last accident was many years ago.

However, the Canadian aircraft operator took steps to change their SAR capability from LIMSAR to full SAR after the accident at the report's recommendation. Some years after the report, the resource company, Shell, made the brave step of providing a full SAR 24-hour operation with a very capable SAR aircraft to its base in Broome, Western Australia. BP would have also offered a similar operation for its proposed South Australian resource operation; however, BP cancelled the oil and gas production project in the Great Australian Bight in 2016.

In some countries, offshore workers travel daily to installations, sometimes hundreds of miles away with only a LIMSAR capability to rescue them in the case of a ditching. The globally recognised standard time of SAR operations is 15 minutes, the wheels up time for LIMSAR is 1–1½ hours. Simple mathematics dictates that even if the aircraft gets off within an hour, which is highly unlikely given the crews may not even be at work or the commercial aircraft configured; a modern heavy helicopter can only fly at an approximate maximum of 145 knots. If the ditched aircraft is 150 nautical miles away, they will arrive on the scene around 2–3 hours after being tasked to assist. The LIMSAR crew must then complete the actual search and rescue from the water with a minimum amount of training.

LIMSAR was the case in the Flight CHI 9 accident, where the offshore operating area is covered by the company's LIMSAR aircraft. The captain of the crashed aircraft advised the company dispatch to get another aircraft ready approximately 10 minutes before the aircraft ditching, which should have given the rescue crew a speedy response to the emergency. Although a fixed-wing aircraft arrived at the crash site 17 minutes after the captain reported he was ditching the aircraft, it was a further 43 minutes until the company's SAR equipped aircraft arrived and another 20 minutes until they recovered the sole survivor.

Despite the lack of mandatory CRM training in the operator's defence, they introduced their own initial and recurrent training. The report states that this demonstrated a solid commitment to safety. The company also had a safety management system in place, which was not mandatory and a just culture ideology. The report also details the company's measures of implementing changes concerning the findings.

This accident was a very significant milestone in Canada's oil and gas resource industry and highlighted several significant findings to be addressed. Utilising the contents of the accident report, I want to begin by taking some of the core elements of CRM and relating them to the accident.

## Human Factors

The report's authors place a great deal of emphasis on Crew Resource Management and the report's factual information on the flight crew; also raises this issue. The flight crew were experienced pilots. From a CRM point of view, the captain is described as being safety conscious, having a strong personality and being assertive in raising any safety concerns.

In comparison, the first officer (FO) was new to civilian aviation, having just joined the operating company from the Canadian Navy less than a year prior. The first officer described as having some CRM issues in the military and these manifested again during his S92 helicopter pilot conversion course. His CRM non-technical skills are discussed and the report states he experienced CRM difficulties during the conversion course with continued improvement in CRM in each session. The FO's previous military training program reports state that the FO's progression was slow due to difficulties with systems and operational knowledge and a lack of assertiveness.

When you combine a pilot, who lacks assertiveness with a strong personality captain, it is never a good combination. In this case, the crew had to deal with an unusual situation with a set of tools that did not help due to many external factors.

## Organisation and culture

There are several breakdowns in the organisational elements of this accident with contributory factors from a national regulatory body, manufacturer, operator and client perspective. Like all accidents, it is a series of situations that, when combined, lead to the accident.

They examined the oversite of crew resource management (CRM) training on a national and local level. At the time of the accident, the regulations stated that operators who were operating under CAR 703 and 704; did not have to provide CRM training to their staff. In simplistic terms, CAR 703 and 704 relates to aircraft operators carrying 19 or fewer passengers, excluding the flight crew.

The report stated that the flight crew had received minimal recurrent CRM training in the time leading up to the accident, approximately three and a half years for the captain and no company training for the FO in his short time with the company. They had received a small amount of CRM training in the simulator, some two hours. The report deemed it unlikely that CRM non-technical skills had been reinforced in this minimal training. In paragraph 13, "Findings as to causes and contributing factors", the report states:

*The captain's fixation on reaching shore combined with the first officer's non-assertiveness prevented concerns about*

*CHI91's flight profile from being incorporated into the captain's decision-making process. The lack of recent, modern, crew resource management (CRM) training likely contributed to the communication and decision-making breakdowns, which led to the selection of an unsafe flight profile.*

If we revisit the error-chain management model from a previous chapter and apply some of the findings to this accident, we can see many external factors that influenced it. In this case, I maintain that if just one of the threat management strategies had been enforced at the time, the accident might still have occurred as there were just so many external influencing factors. What we can see is that in this instance, a lot of organisational factors influenced the outcome. Figure 12a shows just some of the factors that influenced this particular flight; the report gives some 46 findings.

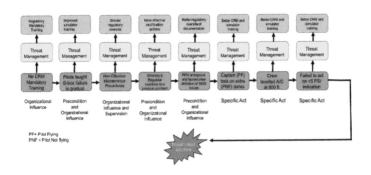

**Figure 12a.** Error chain model

I have been on many flights in recent years where modern automated and glass cockpit aircraft have been introduced into companies that previously operated analogue aeroplanes. I dread the phrase, *Oh, I haven't seen that before*. It is generally about lights or warnings on one of the various glass displays. There is a considerable increase in risk when introducing these aircraft to companies with limited experience in operating modern machines and automation systems.

We may have increased safety with automation; however, we have also introduced a whole new set of threats to aviation safety, which are unknown until they occur. There is a remarkable statement in the movie "Sully" that sums this up. Tom Hanks plays the lead role as Captain Chelsey Sullenberger, the pilot and commander of the A320 that made a water landing on the Hudson River. He is replying to an investigator during the investigation scene who says a double engine failure is unprecedented, 'Everything is unprecedented until it happens for the first time.'

History has shown this to be accurate and yet we forget time and time again. Titanic, "the unsinkable ship", is the best example in history. Its design of 16 compartments with 15 water-tight barrier doors was deemed to make the ship unsinkable. Advertised as such, yet the reality was that the ship could remain afloat with only four of the compartments compromised. The probability of any more being compromised was deemed impossible. Still, as we know, after scraping the iceberg, five of the compartments were damaged and the ship sunk to its watery grave.

During Flight CHI 9, there was a perception that the main gearbox (MGB) had a 30-minute run-dry capability. In layman's terms, helicopters are kept in the air by the main rotor system assisted by the tail rotor to stop torque reaction from making the helicopter spin out. The main gearbox converts the energy from the engines into driving this rotor system and lubrication of this area is critical, as there are a lot of moving parts. In old designs, a loss of lubrication fluid would lead to failure very quickly.

However, the new MGB has various systems designed to redistribute existing oil in the sump or extra fluid to the gearbox. The accepted global standard for time available is 30 minutes from when the main gearbox lubrication container is empty. The phrase used in the standards is the a "30-minute run dry capability".

Before the initial certification tests, the manufacturer's advertisements indicated a 30-minute run-dry capability. After failing to prove this capability, the manufacturer changed the statement to a "30-minute safe operation after an oil leak". The report states that some individuals still believed the aircraft had 30 minutes of run-dry capability at the time of the accident. However, it goes on to say that at least as many people, if not the majority, believed the opposite. During the fateful flight of CHI 91, at no time did the crew state the aircraft had the 30-minute run-dry capability.

Furthermore, the amount of time that the MGB could operate without oil was not in any aircraft manuals or training material. The report states, this critical information would have helped the flight crew in their decision-making process. In the end, the gearbox only lasted approximately 10–11 minutes.

The loss of oil in the MGB during the accident was caused by the failure of two titanium studs, which secured the filter bowl assembly to the MGB. These bolts failed because they suffered galling during maintenance procedures. Galling is damage to metal surfaces that are in sliding contact. It damages the metal by the physical transfer of material, leaving a raised lump (gall). The result of this damage prevented the correct preloading to the stud's installation during maintenance procedures.

Some metals are susceptible to this galling, such as titanium. However, it is still desirable due to its corrosion resistance and lightweight in comparison with steel. Titanium bolts had been used in the same assembly on other aircraft with no adverse effects or reported failure.

Concerning the S92, the maintenance procedure stated the usual number of times the filter bowl assembly was removed; would be five times in the life of the gearbox. However, an additional process called for the assembly to be removed if the filter bypass button popped, indicating a possible oil filter was blocked. In this case, the MGB oil filter had been replaced 11 times using the same bolts each time.

The report states that in its analysis of the safety management system (SMS), the manufacturer failed to identify the risk of using titanium bolts on the MGB filter bowl. During a test in which the loss of lubricant resulted in a catastrophic failure of the MGB, the manufacturer claimed the chances were "extremely remote" under a certification regulation in the USA.

When a similar accident occurred in Australia, the manufacturer's and FAA's communication relied on a new maintenance procedure to mitigate the risk of failure of the nuts and did not require their immediate replacement. Operators had a time period to comply with revision 13 of the Aircraft Maintenance Manual—essentially, just replace the titanium bolts with stainless steel bolts. The Federal Aviation

Administration (FAA) and helicopter manufacturer Sikorsky concluded that except for a potential failure of the oil cooler and its exterior plumbing, all other MGB failures leading to a total loss of oil were "extremely remote".

Often, we will see organisational influences that have the potential to lead to accidents. Commercial pressure, I have noticed, has become a bit of a dirty statement over the years. Companies don't want the employees to believe they are under commercial pressure. Safety has no price; however, the guidance often given to supervisors and middle-management passes on the responsibility of commercial success and safety through key performance indicators (KPI).

The balancing act of commercial success and safety is often handed off as, 'We want you to meet commercial KPI's—however, safety always comes first.' The supervisors and middle management then have the perceived pressure to succeed commercially and somehow keep everyone safe.

Organisation and culture is a relatively new core element in human-factors training, yet it has often been one of the most significant contributors to accidents. As displayed through the Flight CHI 9 accident, organisations mustn't allow perceived pressure to influence safety.

## Teamwork

In aviation, crew resource management (CRM) has a philosophy for managing emergencies. We, as aviators, have it drilled into us from the very beginning of our careers, "Aviate, navigate, communicate" is the phrase commonly used. "Aviate"—to fly the aircraft and keep it in a safe condition. "Navigate"—get yourself to a destination safely.

"Communicate"—inform people if you have a problem and what you are planning so that they can help you.

I have spent many years researching aviation accidents, and a common thread is when crews fail to manage the emergency for various reasons. Often, it is caused by task fixation or a focus on a situation to the detriment of tasks that will keep you safe, such as fuel management. There have been many accidents where the crew have failed to notice they were running out of fuel because they were too focused on a relatively minor problem.

In this accident, the report focuses on the captain's task management. Until the initial indication of a problem, the crew operated the aircraft in the pilot flying (PF) and pilot not flying (PNF) roles, to the company and industry-standard practice. The captain was the PF when the MGB oil-pressure problems became evident; at this stage, he deviated from current CRM practices.

The report tells us that the captain decided to retain the PF duties and elected to take on some of the PNF duties by managing the emergency response and communicating with the ATC and company dispatch centre. It goes on to say that he was reaching a point of task saturation at a rapid rate.

**Task saturation** is where the number of tasks becomes too much for the pilot to handle, their ability to function is impaired. The result includes a loss of situational awareness, the ability to communicate effectively and conduct the aircraft's basic functions. The military describes this phenomenon as "helmet fire", originating from military aviators who wore flying helmets. I remember from my military training that officials will push you to such a point to see how much information overload you can handle.

In flying, you need to apply from memory and those that need to be applied quickly. In the case of CHI 9, they had an initial amber caution message of **MGB OIL PRESS** indicating a low **MGB** oil pressure (between 45psi to 35psi), a sensor records a pressure of less than 24psi. This message appeared momentarily before heading out. Soon, a red **MGB OIL PRESS** warning message (oil pressure below 35psi) and the low-pressure switch is activated, accompanied by an audio message: "Gearbox pressure…gearbox pressure".

The **MGB** has an oil bypass system. This system bypasses the oil cooler if there is a leak in its components and must be switched on within five seconds of the **MGB OIL PRESS** warning.

The captain indicated the MGB needed to go into bypass mode some 11 seconds after the indication and aural warning. He then made the initial mayday call to air traffic control (ATC), followed by a series of events that led to a significant delay in the activation of the bypass, a total of 77 seconds after the initial red warning.

The pilot flying during this phase was so preoccupied with the additional PNF tasks he had undertaken; he failed to notice the PNF's attempts to find the appropriate page in the emergency checklist. On three occasions, he stated he could not find the correct page. The PNF had only flown 13 hours in the previous three months and had less than 100 hours total, which may account for his difficulty locating the correct page. The captain, the PF, had far more experience on type, some 1061 hours. However, he failed to assist the PNF because he was preoccupied with the radio calls to external agencies. Some 152 seconds later, the PNF located the correct page and initiated the checklist responses.

Due to interruptions with the radio calls by the PF, it took 390 seconds to arrive at the "land immediately" line on the checklist. The report states, 'These delays in completing critical tasks made it difficult for the pilots to effectively work through the situation together'. It goes onto say, 'The captain's decision to carry out PF duties, as well as several PNF duties, resulted in excessive workload levels that delayed checklist completion and prevented the captain from recognising critical cues available to him.'

I have studied many papers on cognitive ability under stress and how the brain and our body appear to let us down. Stress hormones are released by our bodies when faced with a dangerous or difficult situation; these stress hormones are messengers that tell our bodies what to do. Each organ of our body has stress hormone receptors, even our brain. The areas in our brain responsible for memory function have the most significant amount of these receptors. When under stress, these hormones can impair our ability to remember things or learn things.

The Checklist design reduces the need for the complete memorising of emergency procedures and helps maintain concentration, essential items that keep you flying. The inability to work together on these checklist items was a significant factor in the breakdown of CRM in this crew.

## Decision making

The report makes many observations on the crew's actions during this emergency and refers to their decision making. A ditching in the sea is a hazardous procedure and something not to be taken lightly by any aircraft commander.

Mainly when the water is a cold and hostile environment; after all, no one intentionally goes for a swim in the cold.

Time was a critical situation, and all helicopter crews know that when there is no oil in the MGB, the gearbox very quickly produces heat and components begin to fail. This will eventually lead to the rotor blades stopping, the things that keep you flying. The helicopter then assumes the flying characteristics of a brick and plummets rapidly towards the sea or ground.

The crew made some appropriate decisions initially—to turn towards land and get lower and prepare their immersion suits. The events following show the pilots had an incomplete mental model of what was occurring. The absence of other indications, such as an MGB high-temperature indication, vibration or unusual noises, led them to believe they had a sensor problem and not a loss of oil.

We spoke about confirmation bias in Chapter 8 as a hazardous attitude—they need to be correct or seek to interpret information that confirms a preconceived outcome. I think the captain's actions seem more similar to a framing error. He based his decision on a more favourable result: making land. Rather than the less favourable option: a ditching. It is easy for armchair commentators to discuss this in the relaxed comfort of their study; however, the two crewmen had a time-critical decision to make under confusing and difficult circumstances.

## Communication

The report looks at the personality types when it examines crew communication: the captain, an experienced and confident pilot with a more direct leadership style. The first officer, an experienced military pilot with a non-assertive personality, had been with the company less than a year at the time of the accident.

They faced a time-critical, unclear and unusual situation. Although both pilots were known to enjoy flying together, these conflicting personality styles became evident. According to the report, the first officer offered several relevant pieces of information to the captain to assist his decision making. The report says that the captain's communication style became direct in its nature; this is easy to do when faced with a situation outside one's normal management scope.

During these attempts to assist the captain, the first officer's background in the navy appeared to show. He had a lot of experience in practising overwater emergencies. He provided relevant information to change the captain's choice to head for land at best possible speed. However, it seems the first officer was not assertive enough in these attempts to assist the captain's situational awareness.

The steep cockpit gradient is mentioned. We have a very commanding and strong aircraft commander who has a notably junior or meek co-pilot, as discussed in Chapter 5—further exacerbated by the first officer's non-assertive personality. If we look at the conversation pie chart below (12b), we can see that in the 10 minutes between the first warning and the loss of electrical power. The captain spent approximately 42% of the time talking to external agencies and just under 40% talking to the first officer. The first officer spoke under 10% of that time to the captain, reinforcing the steep cockpit gradient theory. In contrast, proper CRM training teaches leaders to seek out and encourage input from the team.

When used correctly, the L.I.F.E decision-making tool helps leaders pursue ideas from the team. In leadership, having a basic plan is good enough to have a good team working together to achieve the common goal. As discussed in the chapter on communication, feedback is one of the key ways to maintain situational awareness. A team working on a problem is nearly always better than an individual trying to imagine and implement a plan.

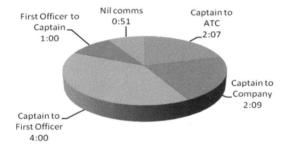

**Figure 12b**
Conversation during flight CHI 9's final moments.

## Leadership

The leadership was strong from the captain, almost to the point of being overbearing and resulting in a refusal to process valuable information from other team members. Effective leadership training is an essential part of CRM training, although often overlooked. Leadership should be continuously assessed during the pilot's simulator training and form part of the line assessment.

## Situational Awareness

Situational awareness comes from a perception of environmental factors concerning time and space. I believe the crew understood the aircraft's position geographically; however, they failed to realise the gravity of the aircraft's mechanical situation and the time available to manage the situation.

This problem exacerbated by the information that would typically aid them, being ambiguous, and couple this with the first officer's non-assertiveness made for a challenging situation.

## Threat and Error Management

The operator had a risk and threat mitigation policy developed into their flight planning system. The flight crew had little perception of just how perilous their situation was and could not manage the threat or errors they were making.

## Health and well-being

The report states that the crew seemed healthy and rested when they reported for duty.

## Conclusion

A tragic accident, with so many contributory factors compounding, into a fateful accident. Almost every core element of CRM came into play during the events leading up to the crash. This accident demonstrates why good, modern CRM training should be essential in aviation. We must learn from these accidents to prevent any more occurring in any industry.

# Chapter 13
# A Case Study

## The UK Ladbroke Rail Disaster

This subsequent case study, I would now like to indulge in, is from the rail industry to see if my theories still apply. This disaster again amassed from a combination of circumstances that formed an error chain, which led to the collision of two trains at nearly full speed. The television documentary "Seconds from Disaster" graphically describes the Paddington accident with a narrative from actual survivors. Thirty-one people died, including the two train drivers, and over 500 people were injured.

The British transport police and the health and safety executive investigated the accident; a public inquiry was also carried out under a senior member of the Scottish Judiciary, Lord Cullen.

Lord Cullen has presided over three reports of significant events in the United Kingdom. The Dunblane School Massacre, the Piper Alpha Disaster and finally, the subject of this chapter; The Ladbroke Grove Rail Disaster. The interesting thing about his report is that it was conducted over two sittings; the first dealt with the accident itself and the second with the organisational safety management. He produced a report on each sitting's subject matter.

# The accident

The Thames three-car train service to Bedwyn Railway Station in Wiltshire left Paddington station in London around 8.06 am on 5 October 1999. The second train involved was a high-speed service from Cheltenham to Paddington. This train had eight coaches and a diesel power car at either end.

Paddington was a busy city station, with numerous lines from the station connecting major and minor destinations in the UK. The routes close to Paddington are bi-directional, allowing signalled trains to travel either up or down the lines. They then connect to more standard twin lines, which only have single directional travel.

Signals controlling the trains in and out of Paddington were quoted as poorly placed and difficult to see. The report states the driver of the Thames train, 31-year-old Michael Hodder, usually acknowledged the signals as per standard procedures. However, on this fateful occasion, when he approached the red stop signal at location SN109, he sped up instead of stopping.

In "Seconds from Disaster", the narrator explains that the sun was low and bright on the day of the accident. The natural light may have affected the signal to appear as an amber warning signal instead of a red stop signal. This phenomenon could explain the young driver's reaction to the signal; unfortunately, the driver did not survive the accident, no one will ever honestly know what happened that morning.

The signalmen, who monitored trains progress through signals, were stationed at Slough. Upon seeing the Thames train run the red, they messaged the train to tell it to stop. The train was already 200m beyond the red signal by the time the action was taken. A further attempt to avoid the disaster was made by sending a message to the high-speed train; this was sent 18 seconds after it should have been.

The signalmen's understanding was to wait for the train to come to a stop of its own accord and, if not, then proceed to send an alert. Their immediate manager backed up this understanding. Further to this, the signalmen had not been adequately trained on the communications system that sent the message and they had never used it in response to a train running a red signal.

## Culture

The organisation and culture of the concerned rail companies and their oversite came under honest criticism. Several reports, audits and previous accident enquiries supplied actions to be addressed. The Cullen report found that necessary measures failed to be implemented due to financial constraints, general apathy and a lack of audit oversite.

Four separate groups had been set up between February 1998 and the accident to reduce the signal passed at danger incidents. A Rail track manager stated to the enquiry, 'So many apparently good people could produce so little action.' He blamed several things, such as over-complex tasks for individuals, lack of competency and a lack of prioritising. They summarised as, 'The culture of the place had gone seriously adrift over many years.'

In his executive summary, Lord Cullen in Chapter 5 of the second report mainly focuses on the leadership and management's role in safety culture.

*The evidence indicated that a high proportion of accidents, incidents and near misses, followed unsafe actions resulting from underlying deficiencies in the management of safety.*

Lord Cullen went on to say that the enquiry heard many definitions of the word "culture" concerning safety culture. When you read the report, it becomes evident that the senior level management gave evidence and discussed this relationship between safety and business.

The counsel to the enquiry gave the following definition of good safety culture:

*The product of individual and group values of attitudes and patterns of behaviour that lead to a commitment to an organisation's health and safety management. Organisations with a positive safety culture are characterised by communication founded on mutual trust, by a shared perception of the importance of safety and by confidence in the efficiency of preventative measures.*

My personal experience in corporate organisations is safety is often talked about as the number one corporate value above profitability. In reality, though, safety does come at a price and often, not the best safety solutions are used; instead, more compromised solutions between finance and safety are sought.

The enquiry goes on to discuss a seminar on employee perspectives on rail safety. The consensus from employees who attended this event was that management was rarely seen, generally only on VIP visits. Mr Kooger, the chief executive of Rail track, a group of companies who owned the majority of stations, rail crossings, signals and bridges, said he spent one hour a day touring the workplace and talking to the employees about safety.

The report advises leaders of such companies in the rail industry to implement a system where senior executives set aside one hour a week to be out in the field with employees. While middle-ranking managers should allocate one hour per day, first-line managers should spend at least 30% of their time on the shop floor.

In principle, a great idea and I fully endorse the concept and can be applied to all industries. Unfortunately, it is challenging to achieve realistically, given the number of work companies produce for lower-end managers. I have been lucky to be in management positions myself; I would take time out to wander into the hanger and talk to staff or phone staff at other bases and find out how things were going. However, other supervisors and managers in the same company may have different priorities, such as paperwork, which seemed impossible to achieve without extending their work hours.

Time management for managers is a subject all on its own and is a skill that managers need to master. Staff need to have a visual presence from the management; if you don't and adopt the cliché of "sitting in Ivory Towers", it sets a difficult barrier. Remember, a manager is still part of a team; if they separate themselves, it is difficult to get the team fully behind them. Therefore, setting time in your schedule for a 20-minute walk around the shop floor should be a priority.

For two reasons, the first, you need to break that chain tying you to your desk. It is not healthy to sit in front of a computer screen all day; one company I had meetings with; put to sleep all their computers every half an hour. The purpose was to make the staff have a break and stand up and walk around for a while. My Apple watch has a function in the health app that monitors the amount of time I get up and stand. It will remind me to stand up if I have been sat down for too long.

The second is to provide a presence from management and allow them or especially you as a leader to monitor and mentor your team. Think of it like creating a meal; many ingredients form the components of the meal. The difference between an exceptional meal and a microwave dinner is the attention to the creation. If you simply place the dinner in the microwave and press start, leave it until the completed bell sounds; you will get an edible meal. However, if you nurture the different components, taste them, add spices or salt and pepper to improve the flavour and turn up or reduce the heat. You create a meal that is beyond just edible but tasty and more importantly, you feel you have achieved something.

The introduction of technology may help reduce paperwork but I have yet to come across a system that achieves this effect. I found that senior management implements staffing levels to the absolute minimum and while you may request extra help are often coupled with a corresponding increase to responsibilities and workload.

The Cullen report provides an excellent statement looking at the relationship between safety and performance, 'The noise around performance must be tempered to ensure it does not swamp the noise around safety.'

## Communication

Communication at all levels is heavily stressed in the Cullen report. There appeared to be a breakdown in communication in many vital areas and these included the dissemination of crucial safety warnings after the incident. An example used was the signal passed at danger (SPAD) warning sheets. Signal SN109 had eight previous cases of SPAD in the preceding six years, yet the driver from that fateful day of the disaster was not aware of any of them.

An interesting argument to come out of the discussion on communication was the confidential reporting of incidents. I have seen many over the years; we had an "any mouse" scheme in the Fleet Air Arm, a collection of small letterboxes and envelopes. I have worked with some companies that provide a confidential hotline, which employees can use to bring up safety concerns. One company had a system of cards to submit for safety issues regarding personal actions or systematic issues. If followed correctly, this process was a great way to have safety issues pointed out; yet some employees saw it as a "tell on your mate" system.

The rail system employed after the accident was called a confidential incident reporting and analysis system (CIRAS). This system developed by ScotRail in 1996 and was later made mandatory for all rail networks by John Prescott, the Deputy Prime Minister, under his transport portfolio.

The argument in paragraph 5.36 of the Cullen report refers to the need for a confidential reporting system if you have already had a just culture? True, if an organisation has an appropriate and just culture and not a blame culture, then there should be no requirement for a confidential reporting system as the employees become empowered to speak up and give assertive communication without fear of reprisal.

The report discusses staff motivation, where an employee seminar told a sad story of staff motivation. Employees were frustrated due to conflicting priorities between performance and safety and manifested in the driver's representatives, who spoke of intolerable pressure to meet on-time performance goals. They also talked of the consequences of deviation from train timetables and the paperwork burden to explain these deviations. The employees also mentioned an increase in the blame culture, which resulted in a loss of confidence and comradeship. Furthermore, with the privatisation of the rail industry, many staff had real issues with job security as many jobs migrated to contracting companies.

When there is low morale and motivation in the workforce, it increases the likelihood of an incident or an accident. When apathy sets in, the incentive and pride in what the employees are doing diminish. A dangerous path, where the rift between the common goal of management and the employee's impression of this goal widens; and the guard slips and the focus on the safety of the employees begin to take a back seat.

## Threat and error management

I have also found that in some companies, there is no "near-miss" reporting system. Near-misses are an active warning of unsafe conditions or a precursor to an undesired state as discussed in the threat and error management chapter. The Du Pont report into rail safety articulately describes why near-misses are a learning opportunity. It emphasises the importance of training management and supervisors in incident and accident investigation techniques, pro-active sharing of information on these near-misses and striving to implement the correct actions in responses.

My principle of pro-active management and appropriate responses to near-misses and incidents as opposed to reactive management and inappropriate responses. The sledgehammer approach combined with a blame culture is a guarantee of employee disengagement.

The training was another aspect mentioned in most media coverage of this disaster. The advent of privatisation resulted in what appears to be and indeed is the case with Thames trains, an inherited training system from British Rail. However, the transition from a government organisation to a commercial or private sector organisation doesn't seem to have occurred without difficulty.

An external auditing company reported:

*The trainers did not appear to be following the training course syllabus and supporting notes as they considered these to be "not fit for purpose" with inappropriate time allowances for some sessions. The traction and introduction to driving section of the course has been extended and the six-week route learning session is being used as additional practical handling.*

Michael Hodder had only completed his training two weeks before the accident. Interestingly, the training manager was not aware of the above perception. Further to this, the trainer quoted above conducted Michael Hodder's training and was not aware of the infringements on the red signal at

SN 109, nor that it was a signal that had multiple SPAD incidents.

The Association of Train Operating Companies stated that training was one of the underlying and recurring complications in this accident and previous major rail accidents. The Cullen report mentions the Japanese Railway training system in which training is part of the culture and integrated training between managers and staff fosters this concept. Furthermore, the Japanese use of daily competency checks, simulators and on-board monitors help improve driver knowledge and train safety.

Suppose we look at the error management model on page 82 and apply the Swiss cheese causation model to this situation. The similarities to the S92 crash we discussed in the last chapter are intriguing. Lack of action after previous incidents alongside training and regulatory body oversites has some level of influence in both accidents.

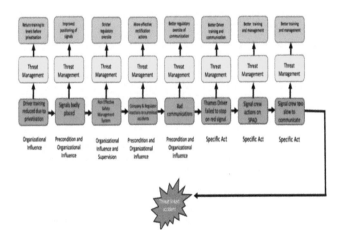

**Figure 15a**

171

## Conclusion

Train safety has improved since and an automatic train stopping system is now in use, which may have prevented this accident if fitted at the time. It was a tragic accident and critical event in the UK that affected many people. Unfortunately, this accident had so many warnings and near misses that it simply got lost in the noise. The various enquiries and investigations have produced thousands of pages of material—the Cullen report parts 1 and 2, which has 522 pages in itself. As humans, we will forever make mistakes, but we must learn from them, which is an evolution of safety.

I see similarities between my industry and the rail industry of the time. For instance, safety culture is a concept and behaviour practised differently at various levels of the organisation. If the management approach to safety is distancing themselves from the shop floor and financial priority over safety, then the message of safety gets lost in the noise of commercial gain, which is a hazardous condition.

# Chapter 14
# A Case Study

## The Costa Concordia disaster

**Figure 15a**
Costa Concordia lying grounded against the Island Giglio

In the previous case studies, we looked at the aviation industry and the rail industry. This final study looks at a very high-profile disaster in the maritime sector, which has been the subject of several television programs. The information, charts, diagrams and photographs included have been kindly supplied by the Ministry of Infrastructure and Transport and the Directorate-General for Rail and Marine Investigations. Particular thanks go to Lt (ITCG) Gianluca La Rosa, who I corresponded with during the writing of this book and who has provided me with so much invaluable information on the disaster.

Like the previous cases, this accident had many significant factors that combined to cause the grounding and subsequent loss of the Costa Concordia. The disaster makes a great case study as the report clearly labels human elements as the main contributing factor. While reading the information, I saw the same elements of human cognitive failure that occur in aviation and other accidents. It puzzles me how a modern cruise ship with all the technology they have readily available could still manage to hit an island.

The sad irony of this disaster is that it occurred almost 100 years after the sinking of the SS Titanic. After looking through the evidence, there are many similarities between both events. Luckily, the loss of life on the Costa Concordia was 32, a slight contrast to the Titanic's surplus of 1500. Although the number may seem insignificant, the lives of the families, friends and colleagues of those 32 victims will forever change.

## A summary:

The Costa Concordia was an Italian-based cruise liner. The ship was built in Genoa, Italy in 2005 at the meek sum of US$570 million (AU$742 million) and owned by the Costa Crociere Group, which is a joint US, British and Italian company based in Genoa. She was the first of the Costa class cruise liners, which the last (Costa Fascinosa) built-in 2012.

On the first night of a week-long cruise around the Mediterranean, the Costa Concordia departed from the port of Civitavecchia. They left just after 7.15 pm on an ominous Friday, the 13 January 2012.

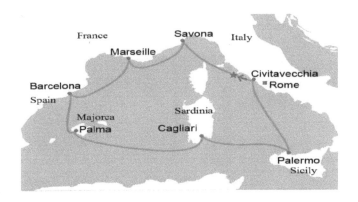

**Figure 16b**

Voyage plan for the Costa Concordia.

Her next scheduled stop would be the port of Savona in North-West Italy. The ship planned to navigate between the Italian mainland and the island of Giglio. At some point, someone instigated a sail past, where the vessel would come close inshore as it passed the harbour town of Porto del Giglio.

At 9.19 pm, the first deck officer calls the Captain as instructed to inform him they are 6nm from the island and will be abeam at 9.44 pm. At 9.34 pm, the Captain arrives on the bridge and orders the helmsman to take the ship under manual control. On the bridge is the standard bridge watch personnel, the Chief Officer, Chief Purser, the Metre (Head Waiter or

Head of House) who came from the island of Giglio and lastly, a guest of the Captain, a dancer.

This modern ship has a vast array of automation and navigation systems and the bridge has a multitude of screens and equipment to display the information. Equipped with an electronic chart display and monitoring system (ECDIS) on the bridge, which, although mandatory now, was not the case at the time of the incident.

**Figure 16c**
The Costa Concordia Bridge
(Picture of the sister ships bridge, the Costa Serena)

The ship had a planned chart registered with the Italian Maritime Rescue Coordination Centre (IRCC). The Captain informed the navigation officer of a route change just before leaving port. The ship's voyage plan shown on a recovered chart from the vessel, displayed in Figure 14d below. The chart is a 1:100 000 scale and was not detailed enough for coastal navigation so close to land, despite possessing an

ECDIS; at the time, paper charts were the only legal form of navigation aid at the time of the accident.

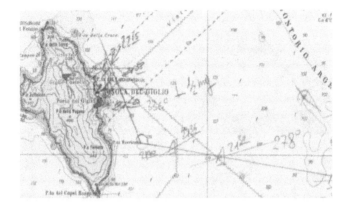

**Figure 16d**
The actual voyage plan of Costa Concordia

The appropriate bridge legal allotment of officers and sailors was present; although some other personnel were also in attendance, against maritime law and procedures. The officer of the watch is legally responsible for navigation; however, the Captain can relieve the officer of the watch with a statement of "taking the guard". The report indicates the bridge team did not properly hand over control of the vessel and then failed to act effectively to monitor the vessel's progress towards shore.

The Captain elected to put the ship into manual control and direct the ship, relying on previous experience. There were many procedural breaches during this phase. Firstly, maritime regulations ban mobile phones from the bridge during the watch and when manoeuvring. However, according to the report, the Captain was engaged in phone communications against the rules. Secondly, no one other than the bridge staff should be on the bridge during critical navigation phases; also ignored.

In comparison with the actual track of the vessel, the planned route shows the Captain passed the turning point, bringing the ship much closer to the island than expected.

## Communication

There was some confusion between the Captain and the helmsman during the event and you can see this miscommunication clearly in the official report extract shown below. Based on the recorded bridge conversations, it seems the helmsman did not assist the Captain as he made numerous mistakes. (The voyage data recorder, VDR, shows when the variable range marker, VRM, circle "touches" the shore it is going to be deactivated).

The Captain now gives orders to the helm for "bows" moves away from the planned course, starting yaw to starboard wider than planned, thus approaching Giglio island.

**9.40 pm** The captain orders in English, '325.'

The helmsman answers to confirm the order, '315.' The first deck officer intervenes to correct the interpretation of the helmsman but pronounces '335', then the Captain reiterates '325'. The helmsman confirms '325.'

The ship is about 0.5 miles from the coast.

**9.21 pm** '330' is ordered and the helmsman answer correctly. The Captain sends the second officer on the left wing, the speed is about 16 knots.

**21.43.08** '335' is ordered.

**21.43.33** '340' is ordered.

**21.43.44** The speed is 15.9 knots. The captain orders always in English, '350,' the helmsman does not confirm properly, repeats, '340.' The order is confirmed again, specifying the side "starboard" and warning that otherwise would end up on the rocks.

From video recordings of the VDR to 9.43 pm, the bow is oriented to 327°. The turn is still in progress at 9.44 pm at N 42°21'0" and E 10°56' with the bow in the direction of Le Scole at 0.3 miles and a speed of 16 knots.

The turning radius is such that the ship is located 0.5 miles South-West of the planned route, much closer to the coast than intended. From this moment, the Captain starts giving orders no longer for bows but for rudder angles.

**21 44 11** 'Starboard 10' (10° to the right).

**21 44 15** 'Starboard 20'.

**21 44 20** 'Hard to starboard' rudder fully starboard).

**21 44 36** At mid-ship (centre) the bow is less than 150m from Scole rock while the ship is off the planned course by more than 809m.

**21 44 43** 'Port 10' (10° to the left). The helmsman reaches only 5°.

**21 44 45** 'Port 20'

After this order the helmsman heads erroneously to starboard to correct himself and go alongside to port as requested by the Captain, then pulling again to the left as requested by the Captain but spends 8 seconds correcting the manoeuvre.

**21 45 05** 'Hard to port' (rudder to the left), the helmsman runs correctly.

The second deck officer from the left wing warns the left side is grounded, a second later there is a loud crash.

**21 45 07** The ship collides with the rocks.

The speed decreases to 8.3 knots, loses propulsion of the two engines and adrift, proceeds with direction of 350°.

**21 45 33** The Captain realises they have collided with the rocks and orders the closing of all watertight doors and aft (the stern). Proceeds to order the helmsman to give all the rudder to the left and after an initial misunderstanding between himself, the first deck officer and the helmsman, this time confirms the order.

**21:45:48** The Captain orders the helm to the centre and the pilot run correctly (VDR).

**21 45 58** VDR communication audio highlights the black out. Rudder pumps remain without electricity.

**21:46:05** The emergency generator that provides power starts only for 41 seconds.

From this moment onwards, the emergency generator is not able to provide electrical power with continuity for the ship's essential services, in particular the rudder and the bilge pump.

**21:46:01** The captain orders rudder to starboard, the helmsman confirms

**21:46:43** Subsequent orders given by the Captain, 'Midship and hard to starboard.' Even if executed will not have effect due to the power failure of the steering pumps by electric energy emergency. The two rudders of the ship remain without control to starboard.

The emergency batteries start but provide only emergency lighting and systems of internal communication.

The ship now has a 53m hole in its side, in which now water pours into the two compartments that hold the six diesel generators (three in each compartment), rendering them useless within a minute. The result is a total ship blackout, uncontrolled and drifting.

The emergency diesel generator (EDG) begins to function but soon stops working after only 41 seconds. This EDG supplies the bilge pumps, which have a high capacity and may have helped the situation. The ships electrical engineers desperately try to restart it and succeed by forcing the switch open with a screwdriver. Although they get it working, they must eventually stop it due to overheating and the risk of a fire. Therefore, it is only operational for around 25 minutes. Some electrical services are available, provided by the ship's batteries but most of the vessel is in blackout and has no propulsion.

The events that unfold after the collision are just as controversial. An announcement made at 9.54 pm to the passengers assured them, 'The situation is under control and the technicians are working to restore the functionality of the ship.'

This is the passenger's first communication from the vessels staff and it takes a long time before the crew finally let the passengers know the gravity of the situation. One of the bizarre rumours is that the music playing over the loudspeakers throughout the ship is the hit from the movie Titanic *My heart will go on.*

## Team Management

The International Maritime Organisation's "safety of life at sea" (SOLAS) regulations originated in the first SOLAS convention in 1914 as a consequence of the Titanic disaster. The latest convention in 1974 formed the basis of modern safety provisions and regulations concerning maritime transport.

The vessel met more than the standard required by the SOLAS regulation; however, the damage was unique in that five watertight compartments were compromised. The company had a safety management system, but the Captain and crew did not follow it. The company had a comprehensive set of emergency procedures, broken down into specific events, i.e. flooding, fire, electrical failure. The fact that the ship had both blackout and flooding may have confused the matter.

Despite the list of the vessel, the severe nature of the grounding and subsequent flooding was not suitably actioned. According to the report, the bridge team knew, six minutes after the grounding, the seriousness of the incident. The general emergency alarm was not made until 48 minutes after the ship hit the island.

The Captain was in contact with the designated person ashore (DPA—the company representative) 12 minutes after the grounding. The Captain told the representative, 'The ship hit a rock with the left side towards the stern...the propellers are not affected and damage assessment is being conducted.' The caster described how the ship was taking on water from the stern and was in a blackout. At this point, the DPA should have encouraged the Captain to abandon the vessel, according to the report.

There were several communications between the ship and the coast guard and harbour captain in Civitavecchia. These communications vary from only suffering a blackout to requesting the assistance of two tugs to the situation is under control. Despite the growing number of messages received onshore by the police and coast guard from concerned relatives.

The first of these reports was received 29 minutes after the grounding at 10.14 pm by MRSC Livorno, from the Carabinieri (Italian military police) in Prato, who had received a call from the mother of a passenger. The call described how her child had phoned to say the roof had partially collapsed in their cabin, the ship was in a blackout and they had been told to don life jackets.

The MRSC contacted the ship and received the reply from the Concordia of, yes, they were in a blackout but required no assistance. However, the MRSC dispatched a patrol boat within two minutes to assess the situation, and it reached the Concordia's position 23 minutes later. The MRSC again contacted the ship at 10.25 pm; this time, the Captain informs them they have a breach, flooding, and the ship is listing. Once more, they do not declare an emergency; only after another call from MRSC and under some insistence does the ship finally declare an emergency.

On the Concordia, a general emergency alarm was given at 10.33 pm and the Captain decided to abandon ship at 10.35 pm. He relayed this to the passengers by asking them to go to their muster stations, not abandon ship. At 10.54 pm, finally, the announcement to abandon ship was given in English. The bridge was abandoned by everyone apart from the second in command at 11.19 pm, who remained to coordinate the evacuation. The Captain left the ship at some point, despite the coast guard contacting him many times to return to the vessel, coordinate the evacuation and give a situation report.

Throughout the night, a massive search and rescue operation took place involving boats and helicopters. The rescue of 4197 people is the success story of this disaster. The ship ended up close to shore (see Figure 14e), which I believe helped this success. Many passengers leapt into the sea and swam ashore or rescued by passing vessels.

**Figure 16e**
The Costa Concordia drifting onto shore, the ship listed considerably more before coming to a stop.

The ships track after the grounding was at the mercy of the wind and tide. It drifted out to sea and then turned towards land (shown in Figure 14f). The Captain stated that his skill allowed this track and the fortunate resting place alongside the island—the coast guard, however, disputed this. The report says that control of the rudders was lost almost immediately due to electrical failure. The rudder pumps one, three and four, ran for only 41 seconds at around 9.46 pm.

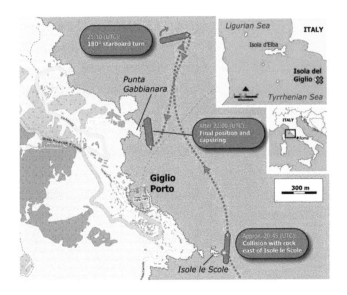

**Figure 16f**
The track of the Costa Concordia after impact.

## Conclusion

The report summary looks at human factors and a lack of competency as the causation of this disaster. The report says that among the Captain's performance errors listed: distractions and violations, which characterised the human factors involved in the disaster.

The bridge team also had distractions and errors during their performance. None of the officers involved had attended a bridge resource management (BRM) course before the accident. One of the recommendations as a result of this accident is for BRM training to become mandatory.

Captain Schettino felt he was made a scapegoat for the disaster; the evidence supports this in the sense that no one on the bridge said anything about the navigation of the vessel so close to land—they just watched. There have been similar incidents in significant airline crashes, where the co-pilots watch the captain crash the aircraft, even though they realise what is happening.

Checklists and procedures are there for a good reason. Science has shown us that humans are prone to make mistakes in stressful situations, sometimes even in non-stressful cases, often it occurs when one deviates from standard procedures. Assertiveness training is a crucial element of human-factors training; speaking up and breaking the chain of events is vital to accident prevention.

# Chapter 15
# A Case Study

## The Rescue 116 Tragedy

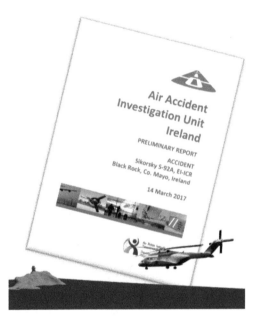

This final case study has similarities with the previous cases. The error chains are also evident and I hope you, the reader, can analyse and benefit from this tragic case. In the last case study, I asked myself how a modern sophisticated ocean liner hit a rock. In this case, I am amazed to ask an almost identical question, how did one of the most sophisticated Search and Rescue (SAR) helicopters in the world hit an island?

The final report was released eventually on the 5th November 2021. As I started to write this some four years since the accident occurred. I find this troublesome that the report has taken so long to be released officially. The information that follows mainly comes from the preliminary report published on April 13, 2017 and information received from my training on the S92 helicopter.

## Background

The Irish coastguard provides aerial rescue services within their SAR region with five S92 helicopters. They have four bases located in Dublin, Waterford, Shannon and Sligo. Each base has one aircraft and a fifth is a roving spare aircraft. Classed as a heavy helicopter, the S92 has a maximum take-off weight of 12020Kg and a capacity to carry 19 passengers. The SAR version of the aircraft has several systems to assist the crew of four in conducting day and night, all-weather SAR missions.

To thoroughly look at this accident, one needs to understand some of the systems this aircraft has to ensure safe and efficient SAR operations. Amongst these systems is an Enhanced Ground Proximity Warning System (EGPWS), this particular system came with modifications for SAR profiles. The system uses GPS information and barometric pressure, and Radar altitude data. A unique GPS-derived altitude called geometric altitude relates GPS information and database information on terrain, man-made obstacles and Heli-pad/runway data obtained by Honeywell.

The system provides a situational enhancement tool for the pilot by displaying an image of terrain as colours on their display. Green represents terrain/obstacles below the aircraft altitude, yellow as terrain near or above aircraft altitude and red as terrain well above aircraft altitude (at least 500ft or higher). The system gives several audio and visual warnings when the aircraft approaches terrain or obstacles provided; they are in the database.

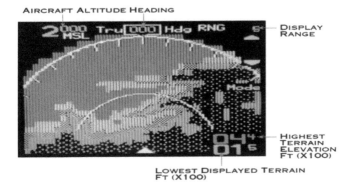

**Figure 16a.**

The EGPWS display (source AAIU report No2017-006)

The computer calculates possible conflicts between the helicopter and terrain or obstacles. It does this by taking data from several on-board systems, including the Radar Altimeter, landing gear position and geographical position. It compares this data with its internal database of terrain, airport data and obstacles. Honeywell, the manufacturer, stated to the investigation team that the lighthouse obstacle nor terrain data for Blackrock Island was in their database on this aircraft.

189

Because SAR helicopters spend a significant amount of time close to the ground, they have a low altitude switch and this switch disables the warnings when selected too on. The pilots would do this if they were flying low level on a search; for example, it would stop the aural warnings from sounding and distracting them.

The aircraft also had an Automatic Flight Control System (AFCS); this system is an autopilot. The pilot's input specified parameters and, when selected, flies the helicopter, maintaining desired height, speed and direction. In addition to standard autopilot functions, it's configured with eight modes for SAR missions. Four modes to assist in taking the aircraft from 2400 feet to a selected height, speed and direction automatically. Three modes for use when the helicopter is in the hover, one of which allows the technical crew to operate the aircraft from a control stick located in the doorway. Used when the pilot cannot see directly below the aircraft and has minimal references to maintain an accurate hover. The final SAR mode's function is the departure mode, which automatically flies the helicopter away from a low level to a specified cruise altitude.

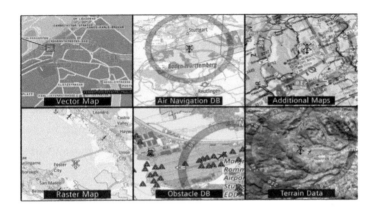

**Figure 16b.**

Various mapping options in Euronav 5 system

(source EUROAVIONICS GmbH)

The Euronav 5 moving map system is a situational awareness package displaying several mapping options (see figure 16b). Full-colour aviation, national recreational maps and vector mapping such as city street maps. It can also show terrain mapping with obstacle avoidance and overlaid terrain information. The Euronav 5 system also has a fantastic database, including airspace information, airport data, obstacles, approach procedure plates and street and road data. The manufacturer provides the maps via a subscription service. Blackrock Island was only on some of the maps in the system, not all of them.

## Mission Background and Timeline

On March 13, 2017 at 2139 hrs, the Captain of a fishing vessel contacted Malin Head rescue centre – informing them they had an injured sailor as a result of being severing the tip of his thumb. The nearest SAR helicopter base was Sligo and at 2142, the Rescue Centre called the duty pilot with details of the situation – the Captain of Rescue 118 then accepted the task. For rescues so far out, 141nm from land (see figure 16c), it is customary to dispatch a "top cover" aircraft to support the rescue helicopter. This top cover aircraft's role is to remain at height and monitor the rescue helicopter throughout. In their National SAR Manual, the Australian Maritime Safety Authority (AMSA) states the following for the role of these aircraft.

The primary tasks of the top cover aircraft will be to:

- Provide navigation assistance to the helicopter to locate the target.
- Provide communications assistance to the helicopter; and
- Provide immediate assistance by way of supply drop should the helicopter ditch.

An Irish Army fixed-wing aircraft would usually conduct this role; however, on this night, none was available.

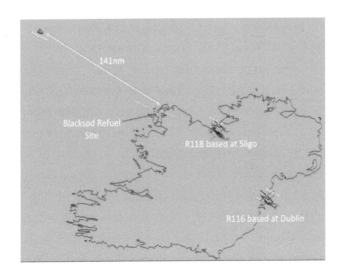

**Figure 16c.**

Map of the aircraft bases and fishing boat's locations

At 2210 the RCC contacted the duty pilot at the Dublin base requesting a top cover aircraft to assist R118; the Captain of Rescue 116 accepted the mission.

R118 departs its Sligo base at 2228; the Captain of R118 planned a route via Blacksod Helo Landing Site (HLS) on the edge of Irelands West Coast; to top up on fuel and then transit out to the fishing vessel.

At 2303 R116 departed Dublin and informed ATC they would either refuel at Sligo or Blacksod on route.

At 2320 R116 informed ATC they would refuel at the Blacksod HLS, as R118 had previously planned.

2311 R118 arrives and lands at Blacksod HLS for fuel and departs for the fishing boat at 2318

R116 climbs to initially 3000ft and then climbs a further 1000ft to 4000ft – to clear high terrain in County Mayo to the East of the refuelling site. From the Cockpit Voice Recorder (CVR), the commander during the transit from Dublin; indicated on a number of occasions to the crew that she had not been to Blacksod for a substantial time. She also asked the co-pilot if he had been to Blacksod recently, to which he replied he had not been there recently.

The commander states to the rest of the crew to complete an APP1 procedure (using the AFCS) prior to turning East towards waypoint BLKMO and then commence an arrival route to Blacksod refuel site. The AFCS system will fly the aircraft from a height (max 2400 feet) to a height of **200 feet** on the radar altimeter and maintain a speed of 80 knots.

The commander programmed the APBSS (Blacksod South) route into the Flight management system during the cruise and had the co-pilot confirm the route matched the operator's route guide (see figure 16d). Note: that the route guide has a height marked as **282** feet for Black Rock Island.

A route guide is a route into a landing site, in this case, on the coast. By following the route, you can safely descend the aircraft from a high level over the sea and then transit it into the landing site via a safe path clear of obstacles. The Flight Management System in the S92 has many pre-programmed routes, which through the AFCS system will automatically fly the aircraft via waypoints at programmed heights and speeds (App 1 200 feet and 80 knots).

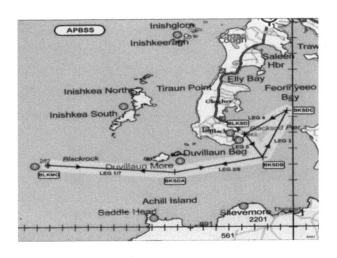

**Figure 16d.**

Company Route Guide (source AAIU report No2017-006)

The system can be overridden to input different heights and speeds. The first method is to push and select the collective trim release under either collective lever; this will capture the current radar altitude and engage the RALT and discontinue the descent. The second method is to push APP 1 switch on either MSP and this deselects APP1 and automatically engage IAS and RALT current values the aircraft is flying.

Note: The AFCS has no obstacle or terrain data input.

To explain the final sequence of the flight, we have taken an Ordnance Survey map and superimposed the helicopter company route guide and the AIS tracking information (see figure 16e). AIS (Automatic Identification System) is a system that sends unit data to, in Ireland, 16 base stations which delivers the data to the Irish Coast Guard with information on the aircraft. This information is the unique identification number, the course and speed over the ground, the latitude and longitude and the GPS altitude.

When south abeam waypoint BKSDA, the crew informed ATC that they had commenced a descent to refuel at Blacksod. The aircraft descends to 2400 feet radar altitude (the maximum capture height for an APP1 approach) heading towards the West. As they approached BLKMO (Black Rock Island) from the East, they turn onto an NW heading.

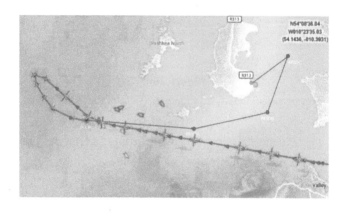

**Figure 16e.**
Aircraft's flight path from AIS tracking information (source AAIU report No2017–006)

Heading North-Westerly, they descend to a radar altitude of 200ft and an indicated airspeed of 80kts utilising the AFCS SAR modes. The aircraft then commenced a left turn onto a South-Easterly heading and the speed manually selected to 75kts. The aircraft commander then requested a "Direct to BLKMO" on the Flight Management System (FMS) – the

Flight Data Recorder (FDR) shows the aircraft commenced a left turn towards BLKMO.

The FDR shows that the aircraft was in stable flight at 200 ft radar altitude with 75kts indicated airspeed (Ground speed approximately 67knots or 30.5M a second). About 13 seconds (roughly 433 metres from the island) before the initial impact, a rear crew member identified an island probably through the EO/IR camera system. He says, 'Looking at an island just in, directly ahead of us now guys, you want to come right (commanders name).'

The commander queries, 'Okay, come right, just confirm?'

The rear crew member says, '20 degrees right, yeah.'

A heading change is initiated using the heading mode, using the AFCS system to create the heading change and not manually adjusting the heading. The rear crew member then interjects with increasing urgency, 'Come right now, come right, COME RIGHT.' In the final seconds, the helicopter pitches up rapidly and impacts with terrain at the Western end of Black Rock and departed from controlled flight. The investigation team identified wreckage and debris on Black Rock, which revealed evidence of contact with the terrain – the wreckage came mainly from the tail rotor and intermediate gearbox areas. The initial impact appears to be with the tail section hitting the island as the aircraft was travelling in an upwards direction. The data from the helicopter recording systems indicates a highly dynamic departure from controlled flight. The preliminary report is very clear from the wreckage description that the final impact with the water was very violent.

The last known AIS position and Flight Data Recorder (FDR) are shown in figure 16f. The wreckage scattered over three main areas. Parts of the tail section on the island itself with evidence of impact from falling debris and striking. Main wreckage on the seabed in 40m of water to the SE of the island, and floating or washed up on the shoreline of County Mayo.

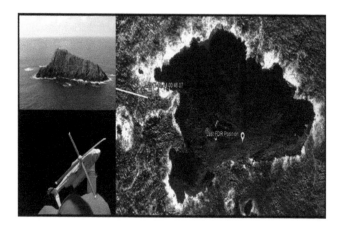

**Figure 16f.**
Blackrock Island and the last known recorded positions (source AAIU report No2017–006)

The Captain was recovered from the sea, and the lifeboat crew administered CPR – she was pronounced dead on arrival at the hospital. The co-pilot was located still in the cockpit wreckage, and the coroner stated that from his injuries, he would have probably died instantly on impact; the two rear crew are currently still missing and presumed dead.

## Additional Data

The actual weather conditions at the time of the accident were not good; however, for SAR missions acceptable. When I conducted SAR missions in the UK, the weather minima requirements was a fully qualified crew in a fully serviceable aircraft similar to the accident aircraft; the aircraft was authorised down to 40 feet, and there were no stipulated weather minima. For training at night 25km from the base, a limit of a 600 feet cloud ceiling and visibility of 4km was in force. The IAAIU report gives the local weather as the following.

Wind: SW at 20knots, gusting 30–35knots

Visibility: 2–3km

Cloud: Overcast with cloud base at 300–400ft

Weather: Mist and drizzle


## Conclusion

The accident deeply affected the global helicopter rescue community, and as part of that community, I was shocked at the outpouring of grief in social media. The facts are clearly stated in this preliminary report and reproduced above. I do not want to allocate blame or cause in this tragedy; that is the investigation team's role from the Irish Air Accident Investigation Unit (IAAIU).

The final report by the Air Accident Investigation Unit Ireland, discusses a number of human factor and organisational issues. What is interesting is they describe this accident as "In effect, what [James Reason] Reason termed 'an organisational accident'".

What are the error chain components, which categories do they come under, Organisational influence, Precondition, Specific Act, or Supervision?

Did the mission have to be conducted there and then, could have it waited for the morning?

I know several people with a very close relationship to this accident, and there is more I feel to it. That aside, the final report is now published and its outcomes, hopefully may give some closure to the families of the crew. This is still a tragedy, and four dedicated professionals have paid the ultimate sacrifice to help their fellow human beings. May the crew of Rescue 116 forever rest in peace; your duty is done.

# Conclusion

I have enjoyed writing this book; in fact, I have found it therapeutic in many ways. It has been serious work, which I hope will bring the human factors in our safety systems to light. Human-factors training has saved both lives and money over the years, yet it has often overlooked in safety management systems up until now. However, it has been part of the compulsory training in aviation for many years because it needed to be.

According to most doctrine on the subject, between 85–95% of accidents are caused by human error. I hope my message or at least the lessons seen in the various examples and four case studies, gives some thought and guidance on human factors and their role in safety to all industries. From the CEO at the top, their senior management team to lower management and the shop floor. As an old friend once said to me, 'The lessons we have learned in our company are real and tangible because they have been written in blood.' While this is true, they are also financial as workplace accidents cost the Australian economy in the financial year 2012/13 was AU$61.8 billion, representing 4.1% of GDP.

In many other industries, human-factor training is embryonic o in the very early stages. The medical industry is such an example, still striving to embrace this message. As we develop and learn from accidents, human-factors training will become a part of safety management systems and integral in the day-to-day training of a company's employees.

In modern society, money is what drives industry; there is always a cost for safety. What is the magic price of an injury or even fatality to a company or organisation? I have heard rumours of the actual price of a life in an industry I had was involved in, which surprised me as the management was quoted as saying that there is no limit to the cost of safety; it seems in reality, there always is.

Human-factors training has tangible benefits to any industry. In corporate language, this is a return on investment (ROI). If we look at a generic manufacturing industry and apply some ROI models, we will see that training can produce significant long-term returns.

The benefits to human-factors training come in two forms: a firm benefit and a subtle benefit. These benefits weighed against the costs of accidents and incidents, i.e. lost workdays and the start-up and running costs of the training program (based on a suitable contracting consultancy and training service).

If you start to research the ROI, you will find it is easy to get a huge return, even with a small organisation. From my research, the average work injury in Australia cost AU$116,000 in the financial year 2012/13; hence even one workplace injury in a small company will affect the company annual turnover significantly.

I did some training last year for a small healthcare company that had experienced some workplace injuries. They also had an incredibly high turnover of staff. If you add recruitment, loss of hours and overtime payments, these costs per annum soon amount. I was shocked when I asked a staff member how many work-injury cases they had in the past year. 'Well, really, we have had at least one person off sick the whole time.' Not all the workplace injuries they described would be a cost to the company AU$116,000.

Companies don't have to pay this total amount because, in Australia, they have WorkCover insurance. However, a company with consistent claims can be penalised indirectly with increases in premiums to this insurance. WorkCover helps with workplace injuries, although there is no financial assistance for replacing staff. My research has shown that the costs of an employee leaving within one year can escalate very quickly. When you look at overtime payments for staff to cover the position, the training costs, advertising, interviewing and recruitment costs go up.

Here I will provide a simple ROI calculation based on realistic costs. Bear in mind, this a ballpark figure and to achieve a truly accurate picture, you need to assess companies individually. Based on 80 staff who have completed an initial course of two days, the table covers all the core elements we've covered—start-up costs, based on a professional human-factors training company's research and course production. The price of a company creating their own in-house training is, of course, somewhat higher.

| Human-factor costs | | HF training costs | |
|---|---|---|---|
| Workplace injuries cost | $49 000 | 80 staff @ 300 per day x2 | $48 000 |
| Equipment damage | $20 000 | Start-up cost | $4 800 |
| Replacement of staff | $87 500 | | |
| Total: | A$156 500 | Total: | A$52 800 |

There are many calculators on ROI; my personal preference is this one:

$$(Probaility\ of\ success\ as\ a\ \% \times HF\ events\ cost )$$
$$- HF\ training\ cost = Return$$

In this example, if we say we only get a 75% chance of success, the numbers are as follows:

$$(75\% \times \$156\ 500 ) - \$52\ 800 = \$25\ 450$$

Human-factors training is a continual process and should have annual refresher training, so the cost-benefit analysis must be calculated over time. Subsequent refresher training can be half-day courses or a one-day refresher course. Half-day courses every six months tend to be more accessible from a staff-planning perspective. The table below shows that the ROI ratio improves with consolidation training; HF training providers may give concessions for a commitment to consolidation training over a period of time.

| | Year 1 | Year 2 | Year 3 | Year 4 | Year 5 |
|---|---|---|---|---|---|
| Events cost | $156 500 | $156 500 | $156 500 | $156 500 | $156 500 |
| Human-factors training costs | $52 800 | $26 400 | $26 400 | $26 400 | $26 400 |
| Return | $64 575 | $90 975 | $90 975 | $90 975 | $90 975 |
| ROI ratio | 1:22 | 3:44 | 3:44 | 3:44 | 3:44 |

Effective human-factors training well integrated within an organisation's safety management system and in conjunction with an active just culture provides both financial and safety benefits. You can even cut the cost of training by going to an established company with appropriately trained facilitators.

There is a growing number of online training providers; my own company has embraced this form of training to stay competitive. However, human-factors training should not be a tick off process. Trained facilitators can identify staff who have human-factor issues and tailor their training to the individual. A computer cannot achieve this without comprehensive psychometric testing software. In my own company, we offer tailored, facilitator-run courses, which comprehensively cover all the aspects of human-factors training and include classroom exercises that test the non-technical skills of the attendees.

The Safe Work Australia report on the cost of workplace injuries and illness also showed cost has effectively doubled since the turn of the century; the ROI and the costs to the nation and industry surely must justify a trend towards human factors training to reduce these excessive costs?

No matter how big a company gets, it will always be a team. As a team, it needs to embrace each aspect of human factors; only then can the team learn how to interact and use their non-technical skills to create a safe and happy workplace. A happy workplace is productive, which keeps industry and a nation's economy running.

CPSIA information can be obtained
at www.ICGtesting.com
Printed in the USA
BVHW091149130423
662288BV00019B/833